P9-BVC-219

Book 2

K¹² Math⁺

Illustrations Credits

All illustrations © K12 Inc. unless otherwise noted
Dartboard. © Artville
Pizza. © Artville
Clock. © m.p. imageart/iStockphoto.com

About K12 Inc.

K12 Inc., a technology-based education company, is the nation's leading provider of proprietary curriculum and online education programs to students in grades K–12. K^{12} provides its curriculum and academic services to online schools, traditional classrooms, blended school programs, and directly to families. K12 Inc. also operates the K^{12} International Academy, an accredited, diploma-granting online private school serving students worldwide. K^{12}'s mission is to provide any child the curriculum and tools to maximize success in life, regardless of geographic, financial, or demographic circumstances. K12 Inc. is accredited by CITA. More information can be found at www.K12.com.

Copyright © 2010 K12 Inc. All rights reserved.

No part of this document may be reproduced or used in any form or by any means, graphic, electronic, or mechanical, including photocopying, recording, taping, and information retrieval systems, without the prior written permission of K12 Inc.

K^{12}° is a registered trademark and the K^{12} logo, xPotential, and Unleash the xPotential are trademarks of K12 Inc.

ISBN: 1-60153-064-1
Printed by RR Donnelley, Roanoke, VA, USA, September 2010, Lot 092010

Contents

Probability and Data

Mathematical Reasoning

Geometry

Rational Numbers

Algebra Thinking

Perimeter and Area Formulas

Probabilities as Fractions

Write a Probability as a Fraction

© K12 Inc. All rights reserved.

Worked Examples

You can write the probability of an event as 0 or 1 or as a fraction between 0 and 1.

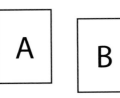 

PROBLEM 1 Use the letters above. What is the probability of choosing a vowel? Write your answer in simplest form.

SOLUTION The vowels shown are A and E. There are 2 vowels out of a total of 6 letters. So the probability is 2 out of 6, or $\frac{2}{6} = \frac{1}{3}$.

ANSWER The probability of choosing a vowel is $\frac{1}{3}$.

PROBLEM 2 Use the letters above. What is the probability of choosing a consonant? Write your answer in simplest form.

SOLUTION The consonants shown are B, C, D, and F. There are 4 consonants out of a total of 6 letters. So the probability is 4 out of 6, or $\frac{4}{6} = \frac{2}{3}$.

ANSWER The probability of choosing a consonant is $\frac{2}{3}$.

PROBLEM 3 Use the letters above. What is the probability of choosing a letter of the alphabet? Write your answer in simplest form.

SOLUTION The letters shown are A, B, C, D, E, and F. There are 6 letters out of a total of 6 letters. So the probability is 6 out of 6, or $\frac{6}{6} = 1$.

ANSWER The probability of choosing a letter is 1.

L E A R N

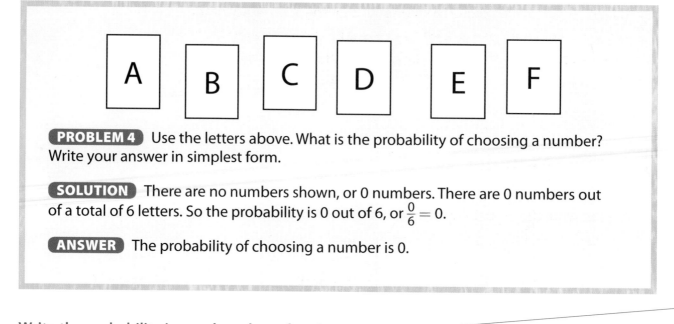

PROBLEM 4 Use the letters above. What is the probability of choosing a number? Write your answer in simplest form.

SOLUTION There are no numbers shown, or 0 numbers. There are 0 numbers out of a total of 6 letters. So the probability is 0 out of 6, or $\frac{0}{6} = 0$.

ANSWER The probability of choosing a number is 0.

Write the probability in words and as a fraction.

1. What is the probability that the spinner will land on a green section?

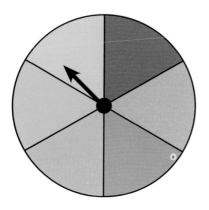

2. Tamara chooses a ball from a jar without looking. The jar contains 3 orange, 4 pink, 1 yellow, and 4 purple balls. What is the probability that Tamara will choose an orange ball?

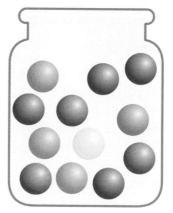

© K12 Inc. All rights reserved.

LEARN

3. Mikel designed and colored a spinner so that the probability of the arrow landing on green is $\frac{1}{6}$. Which one of these spinners did Mikel make? Explain why the others could not be the spinner Mikel made.

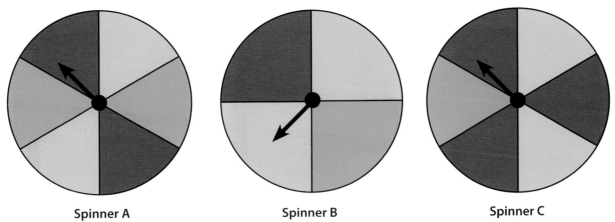

Spinner A   Spinner B   Spinner C

4. Olivia says that for each spinner, the probability of the spinner landing on blue is $\frac{1}{5}$. Is she correct? Explain your reasoning.

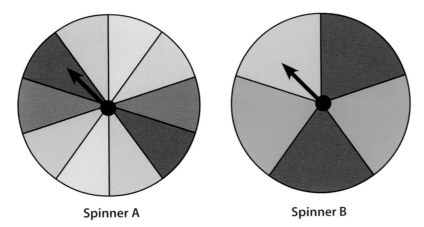

Spinner A   Spinner B

© K12 Inc. All rights reserved.

LEARN

Organize Outcomes

Outcome Chart

L E A R N

Worked Examples

You can make an organized chart to show all the possible outcomes of an event happening in a probability experiment.

PROBLEM Winston tosses a number cube and a penny. The cube's sides are numbered 1, 2, 3, 4, 5, and 6. The penny can show either heads or tails. How many possible outcomes are there?

SOLUTION Make a chart to show all the possible outcomes of Winston's tosses. Then count all the possible outcomes, remembering that tossing a 3 and a heads, for example, is 1 outcome.

Number cube	Penny
1	H
1	T
2	H
2	T
3	H
3	T

Number cube	Penny
4	H
4	T
5	H
5	T
6	H
6	T

ANSWER There are 12 possible outcomes.

© K12 Inc. All rights reserved.

Complete the chart to solve the problem.

1. Marc has two fair spinners. One spinner has the numbers 1, 2, and 3 and the other has an equal number of red and blue sections. Marc spins both spinners. What are all the possible outcomes Marc could spin?

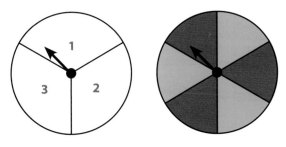

Number spinner	Color spinner
?	?
?	?
?	?
?	?
?	?
?	?

2. Tyler has a bag of letter tiles with the letters T, Y, L, E, R. Tyler reaches into the bag and chooses a letter. He then tosses a coin. What are all the possible outcomes of choosing a letter and tossing the coin? How many outcomes are there?

Letter	Coin
?	?
?	?
?	?
?	?
?	?
?	?
?	?
?	?
?	?
?	?

3. Wendy has three stacks of number cards. Each stack has equal numbers of 4s and 5s, and no other digits. Wendy randomly picks one card from each stack. On the chart below, list all the possible outcomes for the three cards Wendy picks. How many possible outcomes are there?

Stack 1	Stack 2	Stack 3
?	?	?
?	?	?
?	?	?
?	?	?
?	?	?
?	?	?
?	?	?
?	?	?

© K12 Inc. All rights reserved.

L E A R N

4. Jake tosses a number cube and spins a spinner. The number cube has the numbers 1, 2, 3, 4, 5, and 6. The spinner has the letters A, B, and C. What are the possible outcomes of tossing the number cube and spinning the spinner? How many outcomes are there?

Number cube	Spinner
?	?
?	?
?	?
?	?
?	?
?	?

Number cube	Spinner
?	?
?	?
?	?
?	?
?	?
?	?

Number cube	Spinner
?	?
?	?
?	?
?	?
?	?
?	?

© K12 Inc. All rights reserved.

Organize Outcomes

All Possible Outcomes

Read the problem and follow the directions.

1. Miranda spins this spinner and tosses a fair number cube labeled 1, 2, 3, 4, 5, and 6.

   Make a chart to show all possible outcomes. Label the columns "Spinner" and "Number cube."

Spinner	Number cube
?	?
?	?
?	?
?	?
?	?
?	?
?	?
?	?
?	?

Spinner	Number cube
?	?
?	?
?	?
?	?
?	?
?	?
?	?
?	?
?	?

2. Jake decides to have the lunch combo at the deli. He can choose one sandwich, one side dish, and one drink.

   Draw a tree diagram to show all the possible lunches Jake could choose. How many possible lunch combinations are there?

Lunch Combo $7.99		
Sandwich	**Side**	**Drink**
roast beef	carrots	lemonade
veggie	apples	iced tea
chicken	chips	

© K12 Inc. All rights reserved.

T R Y   I T

3. Number Cube A has 1, 2, 3, 4, 5, and 6 on its sides. Number Cube B has 7, 8, 9, 10, 11, and 12 on its sides. List all the possible outcomes of tossing the two number cubes by completing the chart below.

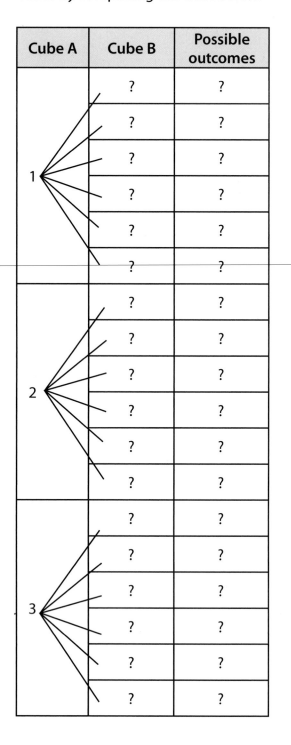

Cube A	Cube B	Possible outcomes
1	?	?
	?	?
	?	?
	?	?
	?	?
	?	?
2	?	?
	?	?
	?	?
	?	?
	?	?
	?	?
3	?	?
	?	?
	?	?
	?	?
	?	?
	?	?

Cube A	Cube B	Possible outcomes
4	?	?
	?	?
	?	?
	?	?
	?	?
	?	?
5	?	?
	?	?
	?	?
	?	?
	?	?
	?	?
6	?	?
	?	?
	?	?
	?	?
	?	?
	?	?

© K12 Inc. All rights reserved.

Choose the answer.

4. Elki has a red sweater and a black sweater. She also has red pants and black pants. Which chart shows all possible combinations Elki could wear?

A.

	Red sweater	Black sweater
Red pants	RR	RB
Black pants	BR	BB

B.

	Red sweater	Black sweater
Red pants	RB	RB
Black pants	RB	RB

C.

	Red sweater	Black sweater
Red pants	RB	RB
Black pants	BR	BR

5. Rande has a tan hat and a white hat. He also has a blue shirt and a gray shirt. Which chart shows all possible combinations Rande could wear?

A.

	Tan hat	White hat
Blue shirt	BT	BW
Gray shirt	GT	GW

B.

	Tan hat	White hat
Blue shirt	BT	BB
Gray shirt	BT	BB

C.

	Tan hat	White hat
Blue shirt	BW	BW
Gray shirt	GW	GT

6. Pippa was baking some muffins. She baked either small or large muffins. She could bake either wheat or bran muffins. Which tree diagram shows all possible combinations of muffins Pippa could bake?

A.
large < wheat small
small < bran large

B.
large < wheat bran
small < wheat bran

C.
large < wheat wheat
small < bran bran

© K12 Inc. All rights reserved.

T R Y   I T

Find All Possible Combinations
Multiply to Find Combinations

Worked Examples

You can make a tree diagram to show all the possible outcomes of an event happening in a probability experiment. To find the number of outcomes, you can count the outcomes or you can multiply.

PROBLEM Destiny has 3 sundresses, 2 pairs of sandals, and 2 hats. How many different combinations of 1 sundress, 1 pair of sandals, and 1 hat can she make?

SOLUTION 1 Make a tree diagram. Then count the number of outcomes listed in the far right column.

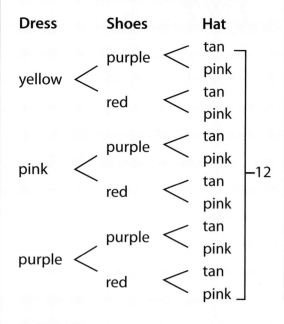

Dress	Shoes	Hat
yellow	purple	tan
		pink
	red	tan
		pink
pink	purple	tan
		pink
	red	tan
		pink
purple	purple	tan
		pink
	red	tan
		pink

—12

SOLUTION 2 Write a multiplication number sentence. Use the number of choices in each group as the factors in the number sentence. Solve.

$$3 \times 2 \times 2 = ?$$
$$3 \times 2 \times 2 = 12$$

Number of dresses		Number of sandal pairs		Number of hats		Number of outcomes
3	×	2	×	2	=	12

ANSWER 12; Destiny can make 12 different combinations.

© K12 Inc. All rights reserved.

LEARN

Write a number sentence to solve the problem. Then solve.

1. You are making sandwiches that each have one type of bread, one filling, and one dressing. How many different combinations of sandwiches can you make using white, rye, or wheat bread; ham, cheese, or turkey filling; and mayonnaise or mustard dressing?

2. Kurt wants to display one of each kind of model he has built. If he has 4 car models, 2 airplane models, and 2 ship models, how many different combinations of 1 car, 1 airplane, and 1 ship does he have?

3. The Diaz family will travel to Oregon, Arizona, or Nevada for vacation. They can drive or take a train, and they can go in June, July, August, or September. How many different combinations of vacations are possible?

4. Hannah is making indoor dish gardens for gifts. She has a begonia plant, a rose plant, and a bamboo plant. For planters, she has a tin container, a brass container, and a copper container, and she has three different types of soil. How many different combinations of indoor dish gardens are possible?

5. You toss a penny, choose a marble from a bag of 5 marbles each of a different color, and spin a spinner with equal yellow and purple sections. How many different outcomes are possible?

© K12 Inc. All rights reserved.

LEARN

Surveys

Survey Questions

Worked Examples

You can conduct a survey to answer questions.

PROBLEM Look at the picture of the softball players. What question could you ask them to find out how many of these players wear hats to practice?

SOLUTION Write a question that could be answered Yes or No. If the question has too many possible answers, it will be difficult to analyze the data.

ANSWER Do you wear a hat to softball practice?

Use the photograph to complete Problems 1–4. Create a tally chart like the one shown to record your questions and answers.

1. Write two Yes or No survey questions you could ask to find out how many of these players are on each team. Use the photograph to answer the questions.

2. Write two Yes or No survey questions you could ask to find out what color uniform, purple or green, the player's team wears. Use the photograph to answer the questions.

3. Write one Yes or No survey question you could ask to find out how many players like to play outfield. Imagine how the players would answer.

4. What other information could you gather from the players? Write two Yes or No survey questions you could ask to gather this information. Imagine how the players would answer.

© K12 Inc. All rights reserved.

LEARN

Softball Survey				
Survey question	Tally: Yes	Frequency: Yes	Tally: No	Frequency: No
?	?	?	?	?
?	?	?	?	?
?	?	?	?	?
?	?	?	?	?
?	?	?	?	?
?	?	?	?	?
?	?	?	?	?

© K12 Inc. All rights reserved.

L E A R N

Surveys
Represent Data

Worked Examples

You can make graphs to show many types of data, including survey data.

PROBLEM 1 Make a line graph to show these survey data.

Daily High Temperatures

Mon. – 75°F	Thurs. – 80°F	Sat. – 82°F
Tues. – 65°F	Fri. – 85°F	Sun. – 75°F
Wed. – 60°F		

SOLUTION Write the title "Daily High Temperatures" for the line graph. Decide on an appropriate scale to show the temperatures. Show the scale on the vertical axis (*y*-axis) and label the axis "Temperature (°F)." Write each day of the week on the horizontal axis (*x*-axis) and label the axis "Day." Make a point to show the temperature for each day and connect the points with line segments.

ANSWER

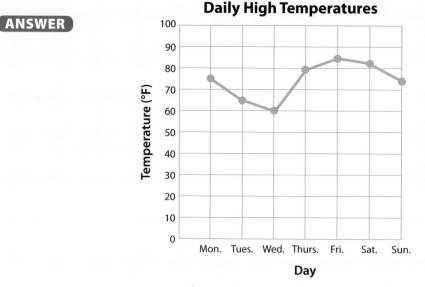

© K12 Inc. All rights reserved.

PROBLEM 2 Make a line plot to show these survey data.

Age of Players on Marisa's Softball Team

Marisa – 9	Linda – 9	Pamela – 12
Tina – 12	Courtney – 8	Eve – 9
Jackie – 10	Jessie – 11	Erin – 11
Lisa – 11	Val – 10	Jill – 9

SOLUTION Write the title "Age of Players on Marisa's Softball Team" for the line plot. Then group the ages of the players. Draw a scale for the ages along a number line and label it "Age (years)." For each player, draw an X above the number that represents that player's age.

ANSWER

Age of Players on Marisa's Softball Team

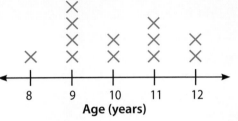

PROBLEM 3 Make a horizontal bar graph to show these survey data.

Favorite Sport

Baseball – 10 votes	Soccer – 8 votes
Basketball – 5 votes	Tennis – 4 votes

SOLUTION Write the title "Favorite Sport" for the bar graph. List the sports on the vertical axis (*y*-axis) and label the axis "Sport." Decide on an appropriate scale to show the number of votes. Show the scale on the horizontal axis (*x*-axis) and label the axis "Votes." Draw a bar for each sport to show the number of votes along the *x*-axis. Leave space between each two bars.

ANSWER

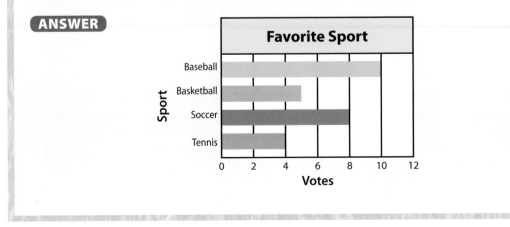

© K12 Inc. All rights reserved.

L E A R N

PROBLEM 4 Make a vertical double bar graph to show these survey data.

Softball Scores at Harper's Field

	Game 1	Game 2	Game 3	Game 4
Home	8	5	7	6
Visitor	6	9	6	10

SOLUTION Write the title "Softball Scores" for the bar graph. Decide on an appropriate scale to show the number of runs scored. Show the scale on the vertical axis (y-axis) and label the axis "Runs scored." List the games on the horizontal axis (x-axis) and label the axis "Games." Make a legend for Home and Visitors. For each game, draw two bars that touch and show the number of runs on the y-axis. Leave space between each pair of bars.

ANSWER

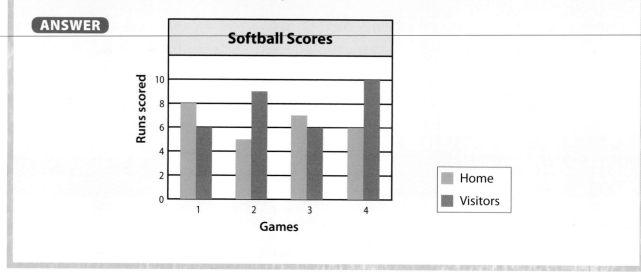

Show the data as directed by the problem.

1. The coach recorded the number of goals scored by players on the soccer team this season.

Mark – 4 goals	Tori – 3 goals
Jeff – 5 goals	Finn – 2 goals
Billy – 2 goals	Hank – 4 goals
Kyle – 2 goals	Miley – 2 goals
Wendy – 1 goal	Adam – 1 goal

    Make a line plot to show the data.

© K12 Inc. All rights reserved.

2. Nicole asked 11 people, "What is your favorite exercise?"
    5 people said bicycling, 2 people said swimming, and 4 people said running.
    Make a bar graph to show the data.

3. Tyler's mom recorded his height as he grew.

    > Birth – 23 inches
    > Age 2 – 34 inches
    > Age 4 – 40 inches
    > Age 6 – 46 inches

    Make a line graph to show the data.

4. The ticket booth at the stadium recorded the number of adult and child
    tickets sold for the first three games of the season.

    > Game 1 – 350 adult tickets, 120 child tickets
    > Game 2 – 325 adult tickets, 150 child tickets
    > Game 3 – 400 adult tickets, 200 child tickets

    Make a double bar graph to show the data.

© K12 Inc. All rights reserved.

Surveys

Data Collection

Read the problem and follow the directions.

1. Matthew is planning to have his teammates over for dinner after Saturday's baseball game. Write a survey question he could ask to help him decide what food to serve.

2. Lily asked boys and girls at Moore Park, "What is your favorite thing about the park?" 15 boys and 10 girls said the hiking trails, 10 boys and 16 girls said the playground, 13 boys and 8 girls said the basketball courts, and 6 boys and 8 girls said the picnic area. Make a double bar graph to show the data.

Choose the answer.

3. Dylan wants to survey his friends to find out which breed of dog they like best. Which question should Dylan ask?

    A. What breed of dog do you have?

    B. What is your favorite breed of dog?

    C. Which breed of dog has the longest fur?

    D. What is your favorite type of pet?

4. Sofia wants to survey her neighbors to find out their thoughts about putting a stop sign on their corner. Which question should Sofia ask?

    A. How many stop signs should we have on our street?

    B. Do you prefer stop signs or yield signs?

    C. Do you want a stop sign on this corner?

    D. Do you always stop at stop signs?

© K12 Inc. All rights reserved.

TRY IT

5. Latanya asked 12 people, "What is your favorite vacation?"
Which tally chart correctly shows this information?

Jeff – visiting relatives
Amiel – camping
Gordon – visiting relatives
Theresa – going to a theme park
Emily – visiting relatives
Akiko – visiting relatives

Gregg – going to a theme park
Cindy – visiting relatives
Marita – camping
Craig – visiting relatives
Suketu – camping
Tim – visiting relatives

A.

Favorite Vacations	
Vacation	Tally
Camping	|||
Visiting relatives	卌 ||
Going to a theme park	||

B.

Favorite Vacations	
Vacation	Tally
Camping	||||
Visiting relatives	卌 ||
Going to a theme park	||

C.

Favorite Vacations	
Vacation	Tally
Camping	|||
Visiting relatives	卌	
Going to a theme park	|||

D.

Favorite Vacations	
Vacation	Tally
Camping	||
Visiting relatives	卌 |||
Going to a theme park	||

© K12 Inc. All rights reserved.

TRY IT

6. Marie asked 12 people, "What is your favorite pizza topping?"
   Which tally chart correctly shows this information?

Riva – mushroom	Marcos – pineapple
Nina – pepperoni	Diego – pepperoni
Mike – pineapple	Lisa – sausage
Sean – pepperoni	Amanda – mushroom
Josh – pepperoni	Terry – olive
Gema – sausage	Ana – pepperoni

A.

Favorite Pizza Topping

Topping	Tally
Mushroom		
Olive	||
Pepperoni	|||||
Pineapple	||
Sausage	||

B.

Favorite Pizza Topping

Topping	Tally
Mushroom	|||||
Olive		
Pepperoni	||
Pineapple	||
Sausage	||

C.

Favorite Pizza Topping

Topping	Tally
Mushroom	||
Olive	||
Pepperoni	|||||
Pineapple		
Sausage	||

D.

Favorite Pizza Topping

Topping	Tally
Mushroom	||
Olive		
Pepperoni	|||||
Pineapple	||
Sausage	||

© K12 Inc. All rights reserved.

TRY IT

7. Diana recorded the amount of time she spent reading her book each day for a week.

Sunday – 15 minutes	Wednesday – 20 minutes	Saturday – 25 minutes
Monday – 25 minutes	Thursday – 30 minutes	
Tuesday – 15 minutes	Friday – 15 minutes	

Which line plot correctly shows this information?

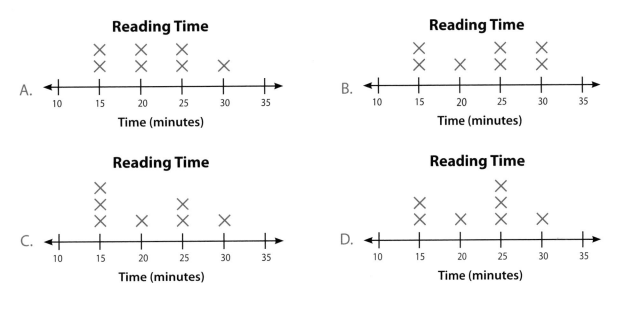

8. Tony wanted to graph these data.

Jill weighs 88 pounds and is 48 inches tall.
Bob weighs 82 pounds and is 53 inches tall.
Nadia weighs 91 pounds and is 52 inches tall.
Gregg weighs 85 pounds and is 50 inches tall.
Kenta weighs 78 pounds and is 50 inches tall.
Sumi weighs 80 pounds and is 48 inches tall.
Marco weighs 78 pounds and is 51 inches tall.
Anne weighs 75 pounds and is 54 inches tall.

Which is the best scale to use when graphing this information
on a double bar graph?

A. 1 row = 1 unit

B. 1 row = 10 units

C. 1 row = 50 units

D. 1 row = 100 units

© K12 Inc. All rights reserved.

TRY IT

9. The cashier at the zoo recorded the number of adults and children who bought tickets over the long weekend.

> Saturday – 150 adults, 225 children
> Sunday – 175 adults, 200 children
> Monday – 150 adults, 275 children

Which double bar graph correctly shows this information?

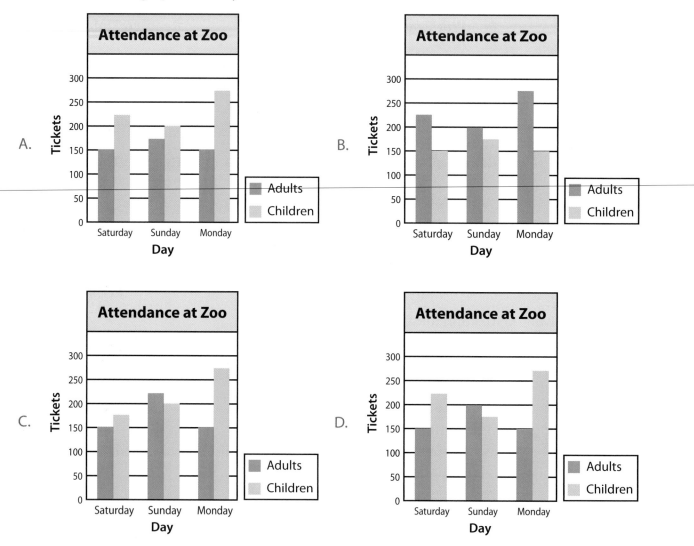

A. B. C. D.

© K12 Inc. All rights reserved.

TRY IT

10. Tayton recorded the total runs scored by his team after each inning of the baseball game.

Inning 1 – 0 runs	Inning 4 – 3 runs	Inning 7 – 9 runs
Inning 2 – 2 runs	Inning 5 – 8 runs	Inning 8 – 9 runs
Inning 3 – 2 runs	Inning 6 – 8 runs	Inning 9 – 9 runs

Which line graph correctly shows this information?

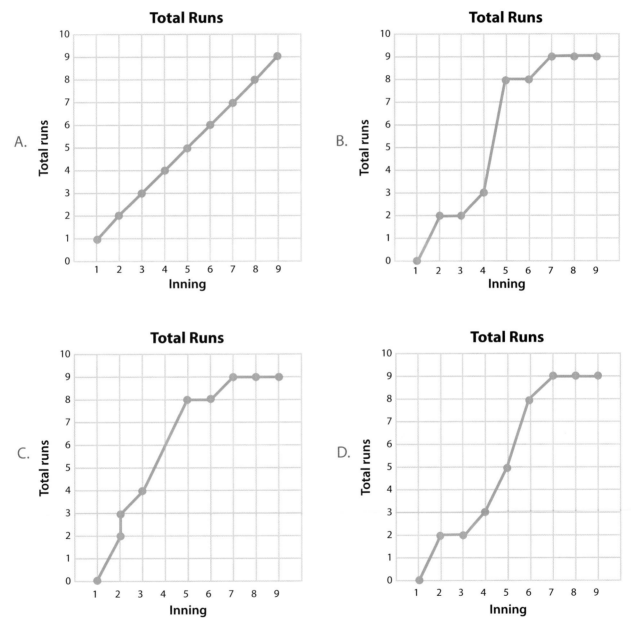

A.

B.

C.

D.

© K12 Inc. All rights reserved.

TRY IT

11. Carlos recorded the number of each type of insect he saw at the park.

Insects	
Ant	|||| |||| |||| ||||
Fly	||||	
Bee	|||| |||| ||
Butterfly	||||	
Ladybug	||||

Which bar graph correctly shows this information?

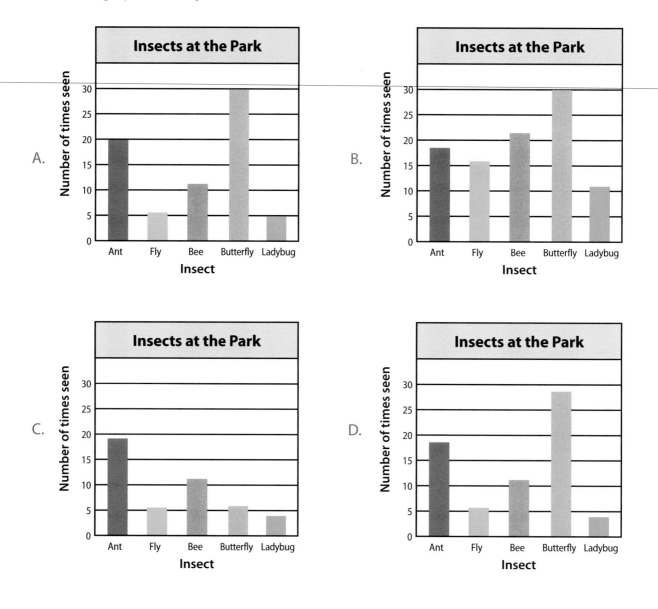

© K12 Inc. All rights reserved.

TRY IT

Data Representations

The Best Data Display

When you have data to display, use the type of graph that best represents the data. Also be sure that your graph has a title, a scale, axis labels, and if necessary, a legend.

PROBLEM For Arbor Day in 2003, Marcus planted a tree in his backyard. Each year he measures the height of the tree and records the data in his notebook. He has made this line graph to display data he has collected.

2003: 32 inches
2004: 40 inches
2005: 47 inches
2006: 58 inches
2007: 64 inches
2008: 70 inches
2009: 72 inches

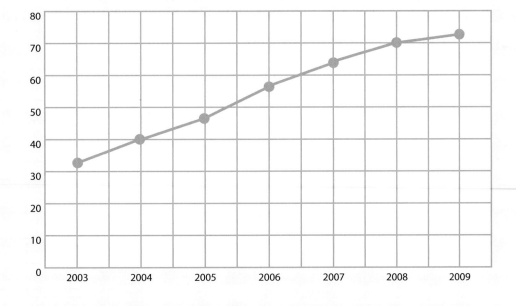

What information is missing from the graph? Fill in the information that is missing. Then explain why the line graph is a good choice for displaying this data.

© K12 Inc. All rights reserved.

LEARN

SOLUTION

1 Check to see that the graph has the following parts:
- Title? No
- Scale? Yes
- Axis labels? No
- Legend? You don't need a legend because the graph only has one line.

2 Decide what the vertical axis (*y*-axis) represents. Write a label.

3 Decide what the horizontal axis (*x*-axis) represents. Write a label.

4 Read the problem again. Write a title.

ANSWER The title and labels for the axes are missing. The label for the *y*-axis could be "Height (inches)." The label for the *x*-axis could be "Year." The title for the graph could be "Height and Growth of Marcus's Tree." The line graph is a good choice because it shows change over time.

Read the problem and follow the directions.

1. Tom collected data about the amount of money children charge to wash cars. He wants to compare the amounts that the children charge, so he created the bar graph shown. Fill in the information that is missing from the bar graph. Explain why the bar graph is a good choice for displaying these data.

Name	Amount	Name	Amount	Name	Amount	Name	Amount
Jackson	$10	Shelly	$8	Aislin	$8	Mark	$8
Alice	$8	Ralph	$7	Maggie	$10	Ivy	$3

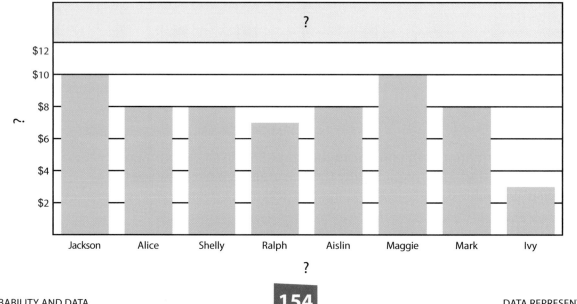

© K12 Inc. All rights reserved.

2. Gregory collected data about the number of sunny days each month.

Month	# of Days
January	17
February	16
March	17
April	18
May	20
June	25
July	27
August	26
September	23
October	20
November	18
December	16

On the next page are three ways to display the data.
Which data display do you think best shows the data?
Explain your answer.

© K12 Inc. All rights reserved.

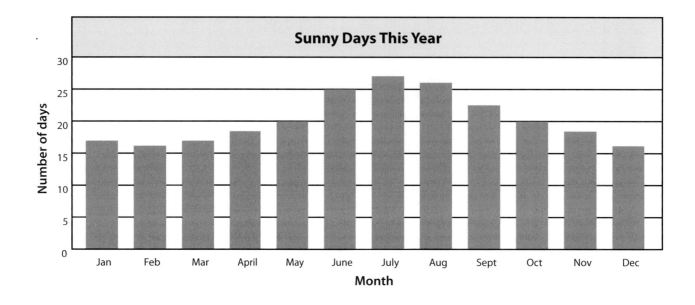

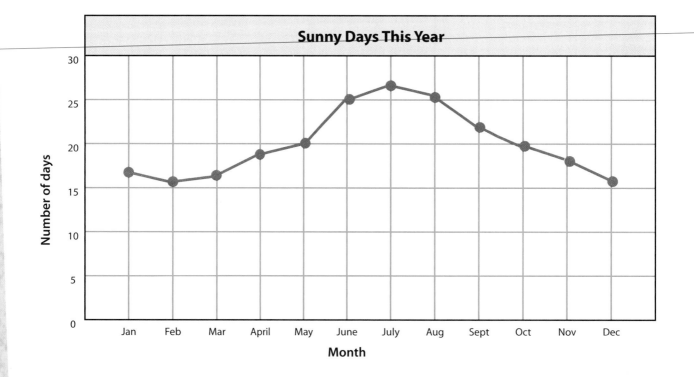

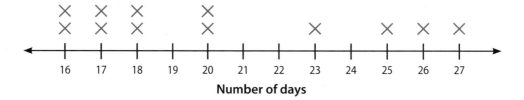

© K12 Inc. All rights reserved.

LEARN

Choose the answer.

3. Louise collected the following data about the favorite colors of some boys and girls.

Color	# of boys	# of girls	Color	# of boys	# of girls
Orange	50	49	Green	27	13
Purple	34	21	Red	3	19

Which data display best represents the data?

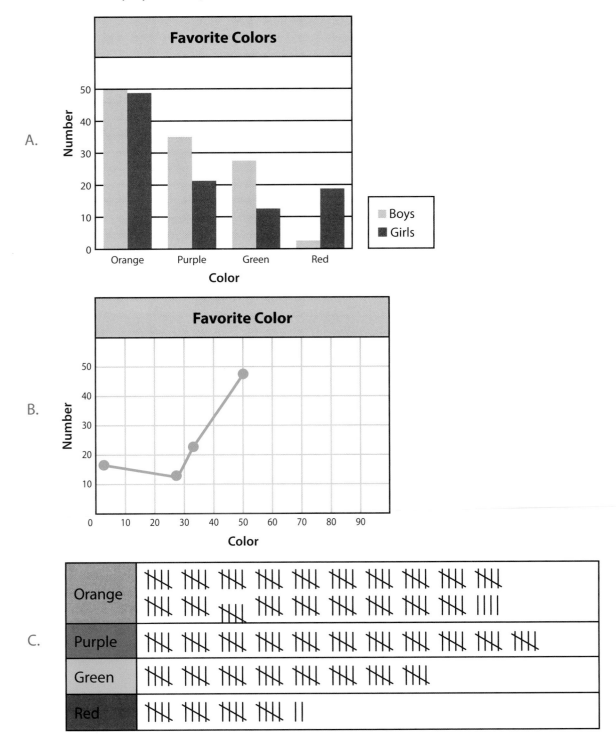

© K12 Inc. All rights reserved.

4. Halle collected the following data about the number of miles she ran each day.

Day	# of miles	Day	# of miles	Day	# of miles	Day	# of miles
Day 1	4	Day 3	4	Day 5	3	Day 7	5
Day 2	6	Day 4	2	Day 6	4		

Which data display best shows the number of miles that occurs most often?

A.

Day 1	||||	Day 5	|||
Day 2	卌 |	Day 6	||||
Day 3	||||	Day 7	卌
Day 4	||		

B.

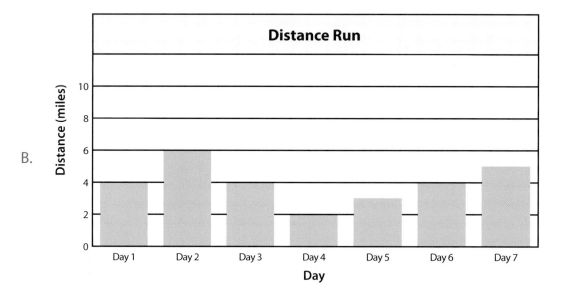

C.

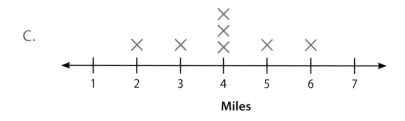

© K12 Inc. All rights reserved.

Data Representations

Data Display Selection

Choose the answer.

1. Chelsea collected the following data about the number of days that it rained each month.

Month	# of Days	Month	# of Days	Month	# of Days
January	3	May	6	September	1
February	5	June	3	October	3
March	3	July	no rain	November	5
April	3	August	2	December	3

Which data display best represents the data?

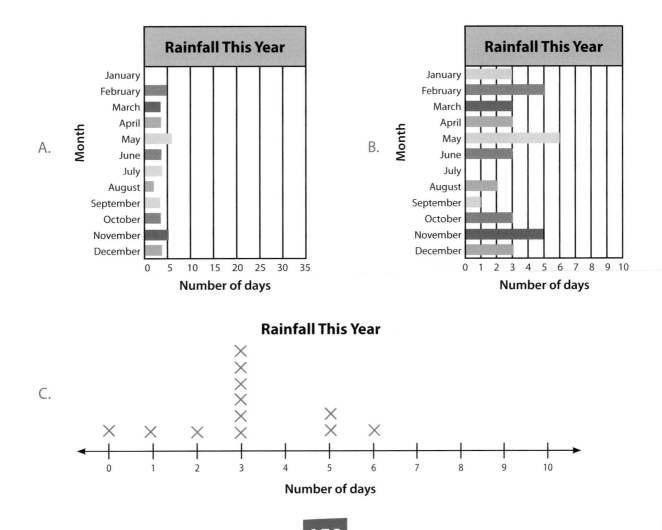

© K12 Inc. All rights reserved.

TRY IT

2. Jenelle collected the following data about the number of boys and girls playing different sports.

Sport	# of boys	# of girls	Sport	# of boys	# of girls
Soccer	53	49	Ice hockey	27	13
Baseball	34	21	Field hockey	3	19

Which graph best represents the data?

A.

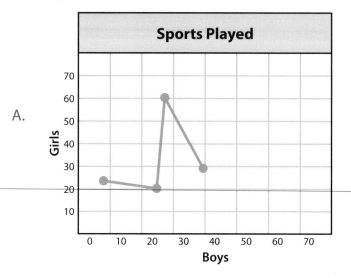

B.

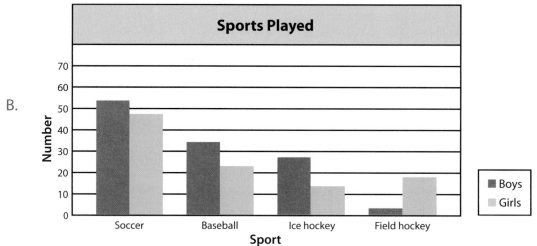

C.

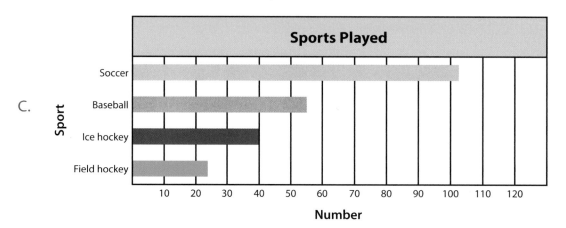

© K12 Inc. All rights reserved.

3. Tom collected the following data about the amount other children were charging to wash cars.

Name	Amount	Name	Amount	Name	Amount	Name	Amount
Jackson	$10	Shelly	$8	Aislin	$8	Mark	$8
Alice	$8	Ralph	$7	Maggie	$10	Ivy	$3

Which data display is used to show the amount that occurs most often?

A.

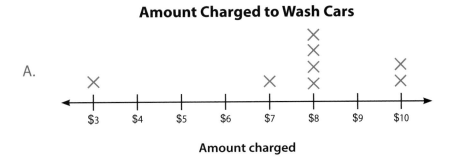

Amount Charged to Wash Cars

Amount charged

B.

Jackson	卌 卌	Aislin	卌 |||
Alice	卌 |||	Maggie	卌 卌
Shelly	卌 |||	Mark	卌 |||
Ralph	卌 ||	Ivy	|||

© K12 Inc. All rights reserved.

TRY IT

4. Kent wanted to know if he would do better on tests if he spent more time doing his homework. Kent collected the following data.

Subject	Time	Score	Subject	Time	Score	Subject	Time	Score
Math	30 min	10	Math	10 min	5	Reading	15 min	7
Spelling	15 min	6	Math	20 min	7	Spelling	15 min	5
Math	25 min	8	Spelling	25 min	9			

Which data display will best show this information?

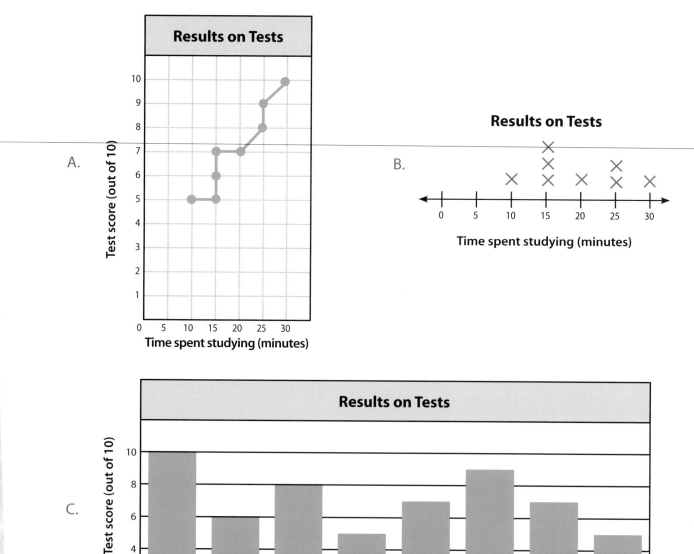

A.

B.

C.

© K12 Inc. All rights reserved.

5. Gina wanted to know if her sunflowers would grow taller if she gave them more water. Gina collected the following data.

Water	Growth	Water	Growth
10 mL	2 cm	15 mL	4 cm
5 mL	1 cm	10 mL	3 cm
20 mL	5 cm		

Which data display will best show this information?

A.

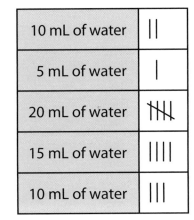

B.

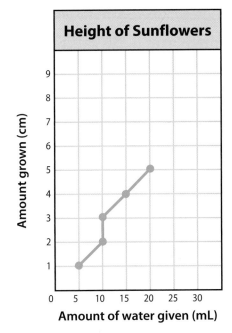

C.

Height of Sunflowers

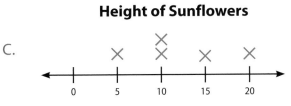

Amount of growth (cm)

© K12 Inc. All rights reserved.

TRY IT

Analyze Story Problems (B)

Use a Problem-Solving Plan

Worked Examples

You can use a 4-step problem-solving plan to solve a story problem. When you solve a multistep problem, you can break it into simpler parts.

PROBLEM Hannah is at a choir concert. The choir sings 5 songs that are each about 3 minutes long. The choir stands in two different sections with 6 rows in each section. In the first section, there are 5 members in each row. In the second section, there are 6 members in each row. Three-fifths of the choir members are girls. The rest are boys. How many members are there in the choir?

SOLUTION

UNDERSTAND THE PROBLEM You need to find out how many members there are in the choir. First you need to find out how many members stand in each of the sections.

You do **not** need to know how many songs the choir sings, how long each song is, or how many choir members are girls or boys.

DEVISE A PLAN

1 Find the number of choir members that stand in the first section.

2 Find the number of choir members that stand in the second section.

3 Write a number sentence to find the total number of choir members that stand in both sections. Then solve.

CARRY OUT THE PLAN

1 There are 6 rows in the first section. 5 choir members stand in each row.
Multiply 6 rows by 5 choir members per row.
$6 \times 5 = 30$; 30 choir members

2 There are 6 rows in the second section. 6 choir members stand in each row.
Multiply 6 rows by 6 choir members per row.
$6 \times 6 = 36$; 36 choir members

3 $30 + 36 = ?$
30 choir members + 36 choir members = 66 choir members

© K12 Inc. All rights reserved.

LEARN

LOOK BACK Make sure you've answered the question that was asked. You can use opposite operations, or inverse operations, to check your work.

- Does 6 rows × 5 choir members = 30 choir members?
  Yes, because $30 \div 5 = 6$.
- Does 6 rows × 6 choir members = 36 choir members?
  Yes, because $36 \div 6 = 6$.
- Does $30 + 36 = 66$ choir members?
  Yes, because $66 - 36 = 30$.

So the correct answer is 66 choir members.

ANSWER There are 66 members in the choir.

Solve. Use the problem-solving plan; show how you looked back to check your answer.

1. Stephen is planning a party for 13 people. Everyone will have 30 minutes to eat dinner. He will serve pizza. 1 pizza feeds 6 people. During the party, he wants to play 3 games. 2 of the games will take 15 minutes each. 1 game will take 20 minutes. He will give each guest 2 party favors. Stephen will start the activities of the party 10 minutes after it starts to give all his guests a chance to arrive. Stephen wants his party to end at 8:00 p.m.

    At what time should Stephen's party start?

2. Yolanda, Jerry, and Sarah collect trading cards. A card box holds 35 cards. A card album holds 40 cards. Yolanda has 45 cards. Jerry has an album full of cards. Sarah has two full boxes of cards.

    How many more cards would Yolanda have to get to have the same number of cards as Sarah?

© K12 Inc. All rights reserved.

L E A R N

Analyze Story Problems (B)

Solve Problems

Explain the steps to solve the problem.

1. The baker used 52 cups of white flour, 13 cups of wheat flour, and 7 cups of sugar every day.

    How much flour did the baker use in 5 days?

Identify the information that is necessary to solve the problem.

2. Margaret curls up on the sofa and reads for 30 minutes and then plays outside for 45 minutes on Saturday and 45 minutes on Sunday.

    For how many minutes does Margaret play outside on the weekend?

Choose the plan that solves the problem.

3. Sarah is assembling 1 bag for each of 7 participants in a competition. She puts 2 shirts and 12 pins in each bag. In each bag she also puts 3 instructions packets.

    How many shirts and pins did Sarah put in the bags altogether?

    A. Add the number of shirts in each bag to 7. Add the number of pins in each bag to 7. Then add those sums.

    B. Add the number of shirts in each bag to the number of pins in each bag. Multiply that sum by 7.

    C. Multiply the number of shirts in each bag by 7. Multiply the number of pins in each bag by 3. Then add those products.

4. Solei washed 3 loads of laundry on the weekend and 2 loads of laundry during the week. Each load takes 35 minutes to wash and uses 5 gallons of water per load.

    How much water did Solei use to do his laundry?

    A. **Step 1:** Add $3 + 2$.
        Step 2: Multiply the sum by 35.

    B. **Step 1:** Add $3 + 2$.
        Step 2: Multiply the sum by 5.

    C. **Step 1:** Multiply 3×5.
        Step 2: Add 35 to the product.

    D. **Step 1:** Multiply 2×35.
        Step 2: Add 5 to the product.

© K12 Inc. All rights reserved.

TRY IT

Multistep Problems

Solve Multistep Problems

© K12 Inc. All rights reserved.

Worked Examples

You can use the problem-solving plan to solve a story problem. To solve a multistep problem, you can break it into simpler parts.

PROBLEM Mr. Zimmer is building steps to his porch. He needs 4 boards that are 12 feet long. He needs 6 boards that are 18 feet long. How many feet of board does Mr. Zimmer need in all?

SOLUTION

UNDERSTAND THE PROBLEM You need to find out how many total feet of board Mr. Zimmer needs to build the steps. First, find out how many feet are in four 12-foot-long boards and in six 18-foot-long boards.

DEVISE A PLAN Break this multistep problem into simpler parts.

1 Find the number of feet in four 12-foot-long boards.

2 Find the number of feet in six 18-foot-long boards.

3 Write a number sentence to find the total number of feet of board Mr. Zimmer needs. Then solve.

CARRY OUT THE PLAN

1 There are 4 boards. Each board is 12 feet long.
Multiply 4 boards by 12 feet per board.
$4 \times 12 = 48$; 48 feet

2 There are 6 boards. Each board is 18 feet long.
Multiply 6 boards by 18 feet per board.
$6 \times 18 = 108$; 108 feet

3 $48 + 108 = ?$
48 feet + 108 feet = 156 feet

LOOK BACK Make sure you've answered the question that was asked. Estimate the answer, about 150 feet (50 feet + 100 feet = 150 feet.) Since 156 feet is close to the estimate of 150 feet, the answer makes sense.

ANSWER Mr. Zimmer needs 156 feet of board.

L E A R N

Use this story problem to solve Problems 1 and 2.

Katie is having a party. She wants to tape paper streamers from the ceiling. Each red streamer is 6 feet long and each yellow streamer is 7 feet long. If Katie hangs 10 red streamers and 7 yellow streamers, how many feet of paper streamers will she use altogether?

1. What are the simpler parts of the problem?

2. What is the answer to the problem?

Use this story problem to solve Problems 3 and 4.

Josh needs to buy 4 cans of paint. Al's Paint and Go sells paint for $11.50 a can. Bob's Paint Shop sells paint for $22 for 2 cans. Mazzeo's Paint and Stuff sells paint for $48 for 4 cans. At which store is the paint the least expensive? How much will Josh save by buying the paint at that store rather than either of the other two stores?

3. What are the simpler parts of the problem?

4. What is the answer to the problem?

Use this story problem to solve Problems 5 and 6.

Tyson and Jonathan go to the Snack Shack for lunch. Tyson buys a special, a chef salad, and a large drink. Jonathan buys two specials. Who spends more? How much more?

5. What are the simpler parts of the problem?

6. What is the answer to the problem?

Menu	
Chef Salad	$5.50
Hamburger	$4.25
Hot Dog	$3.75
Chicken Sandwich	$4.50

Drink
  small
  medium
  large
	$0.75
	$1.15
	$1.25

Chips	$1.00
Special = 1 meal + medium drink + chips	$6.50

© K12 Inc. All rights reserved.

LEARN

Estimate to Predict and Verify (A)

Estimate with Mental Math

Worked Examples

You can estimate to solve a story problem that does not require an exact answer.

PROBLEM Last week a 747 jet airliner made 18 flights with no empty seats. If each flight carried 222 passengers, about how many passengers did the airliner carry last week?

SOLUTION

UNDERSTAND THE PROBLEM The question is, "About how many passengers did the airliner carry last week?" So the answer should be an estimate, not an exact solution.

DEVISE A PLAN You need to break the problem into three parts. Use friendly numbers to round. Use mental math to solve.

1 Round the number of flights to the nearest ten.

2 Round the number of passengers per flight to the nearest hundred.

3 Write a number sentence to multiply the estimated number of flights × the estimated number of passengers. Then solve.

CARRY OUT THE PLAN

1 Round 18 flights to 20 flights.

2 Round 222 passengers to 200 passengers.

3 $20 \times 200 = ?$
$20 \times 200 = 4,000$; The airliner carried about 4,000 passengers last week.

LOOK BACK Reread the problem to be sure you answered the question. Use a number line or place-value chart to be sure you rounded correctly. Then use the inverse operation of division to check your calculation. Does $4,000 \div 20 = 200$? Yes.

ANSWER The airliner carried about 4,000 passengers.

© K12 Inc. All rights reserved.

L E A R N

Write a number sentence you can use to estimate the answer.
Then solve.

1. Last week a 747 jet airliner made 9 flights with no empty seats. If 1,998 passengers flew on the jet last week, about how many passengers were on each flight?

2. A flower shop has 4,867 carnations to tie in bunches with 7 carnations in each bunch. About how many bunches of carnations will the flower shop have?

3. The best tickets to one New York City play cost $288 each. If 42 people buy those tickets, about how much money will the box office collect for the best tickets?

4. During the first week of the county fair, 19,793 people attended the fair. During the second week of the fair, 13,123 attended. About how many people attended the county fair during its first two weeks?

5. During the first two weeks of the county fair, 23,028 people used student passes and 9,888 people used paid tickets. About how many more people used student passes than paid tickets?

© K12 Inc. All rights reserved.

LEARN

Estimate to Predict and Verify (A)

Estimation with Story Problems

Read the problem and follow the directions.

1. In 2009, the population of a small city was 45,925.
   If the population were to decrease by 1,099 people in the next
   5 years, what would the population be in 2014?

   Use estimation to predict the answer to the nearest thousand.

Choose the answer.

2. A stamp collector has 1,176 stamps from 6 different countries.
   He has an equal number of stamps from each country.
   How many stamps does the stamp collector have from each country?

   Which estimation can you use to estimate the answer to the story problem?

   A. $1,800 \div 6$ B. $1,200 \div 6$

   C. $1,200 \div 5$ D. $1,299 \times 6$

3. A bird-watching club has an outing once a year. The members counted
   469 birds the first year, 613 birds the second year, and 555 birds the
   third year. A student answered that the club saw 1,537 birds in the
   3 years of bird-watching outings.

   Which statement about the student's answer is correct?

   A. The answer should be about 1,600. The student's answer is not correct.

   B. The answer should be about 1,500. The student's answer is correct.

   C. The answer should be about 15,000. The student's answer is not correct.

   D. The answer should be about 16,000. The student's answer is not correct.

4. A theater group sold tickets for 29 days before the performance.
   If the group sold 87 tickets each day, about how many tickets
   did the members sell in the 29 days?

   Which answer will give the most accurate estimation?

   A. $90 + 30$ B. 80×30

   C. $90 \div 30$ D. 90×30

© K12 Inc. All rights reserved.

TRY IT

Estimate to Predict and Verify (B)

Analyze and Solve Story Problems

Worked Examples

You can estimate the answer to a story problem. Then you can solve the problem and compare your exact answer to your estimate. If the two values are close, then your answer is reasonable.

PROBLEM An office building with 8 floors has 39 lamps on each floor. Each lamp holds 1 light bulb. The building owner is replacing old light bulbs with energy-saving bulbs. So far, she has replaced 53 bulbs. How many bulbs does she still need to replace?

SOLUTION

UNDERSTAND THE PROBLEM You need to find out how many light bulbs the building manager still needs to replace after she replaces 53 bulbs. But first you need to find out how many total lamps are in the building.

DEVISE A PLAN This is a multistep problem. You need to break the problem into three parts.

1. Estimate the answer to the story problem.

2. Find the number of lamps, each needing 1 light bulb.

3. Write a number sentence to subtract 53 from the total number of lamps. Then solve.

CARRY OUT THE PLAN

1. Round 39 to 40. There are about 40 lamps on each floor. There are 8 floors. Use mental math to multiply $40 \times 8 = 320$. So you know there are about 320 lamps in all. Round 53 to 50. About 50 bulbs have been replaced.
$320 - 50 = ?$; $320 - 50 = 270$; About 270 light bulbs still need to be replaced

2. There are 39 lamps on each floor with 1 bulb in each lamp. $39 \times 1 = 39$
There are 8 floors with 39 bulbs to replace on each floor. $8 \times 39 = 312$
So there are 312 lamps in the building.

3. $312 - 53 = ?$; $312 - 53 = 259$

© K12 Inc. All rights reserved.

L E A R N

LOOK BACK Compare the exact answer to the estimate. Since an answer of 259 light bulbs is fairly close to the estimate of 270 light bulbs, then the answer is reasonable but should be checked again for accuracy.

ANSWER The building manager still needs to replace 259 light bulbs.

Estimate the answer, and then solve. Use the estimate to explain why the answer is reasonable.

1. How many yards of rope are needed to make eighteen 6-foot jump ropes and thirty-one 9-foot jump ropes? There are 3 feet in 1 yard.

   Estimate?
   Exact answer?
   Explanation?

2. A farmer has 9 cartons of potatoes. Each carton weighs 59 pounds. If all the potatoes are about the same weight and size, how many 3-pound bags of potatoes can the farmer make?

   Estimate?
   Exact answer?
   Explanation?

3. A restaurant has 19 inside tables that can each seat 6 people. It has 11 outside tables that can each seat 4 people. How many total people can be seated inside and outside the restaurant?

   Estimate?
   Exact answer?
   Explanation?

© K12 Inc. All rights reserved.

L E A R N

Estimate to Predict and Verify (B)

Solve Problems with Data from Tables

Worked Examples

You can solve story problems with data from tables. You can compare your exact answer to an estimate, or prediction, to be sure your answer is reasonable.

PROBLEM Steve buys 93 bags of doggie treats. He repackages them in 9-ounce portions. How many portions will he have?

Treats	Price
Doggie Treat 21 oz bag	$3.80

SOLUTION

UNDERSTAND THE PROBLEM The problem is asking how many 9-ounce portions of doggie treats Steve will have.

DEVISE A PLAN This is a multistep problem. Break the problem into three parts. Use the information in the table to solve one or more of the parts.

1 Make a written estimate.

2 Find the number of ounces of doggie treats that Steve has in all.

3 Write a number sentence to divide the total ounces of doggie treats into 9-ounce portions. Then solve.

CARRY OUT THE PLAN

1 Round 93 to 90. Steve buys about 90 bags of treats.
Round 21 to 20. Each bag holds about 20 ounces of treats.
90×20 ounces $= 1,800$; Steve has about 1,800 ounces of treats in all.
Each portion is 9 ounces. Mentally divide $1,800 \div 9 = 200$.
Estimate: Steve has about 200 portions.

2 Each bag has 21 ounces of treats.
93×21 ounces $= 1,953$ ounces

3 1,953 ounces $\div 9 = ?$; 1,953 ounces $\div 9 = 217$; Exact answer: 217 bags

LOOK BACK Compare the estimate to the exact answer. The exact answer of 217 bags is close to the estimate of 200 bags, so it is a reasonable answer.

ANSWER Steve can make 217 bags of doggie treats.

© K12 Inc. All rights reserved.

LEARN

Use the tables to solve. First write the estimate. Then write the exact answer.

Dog gates	Sale price
77-inch flexible gate	$115
24-inch gate extension	$35

Collars	Plain	With name
Small	$4	$17
Medium	$6	$18
Large	$7	$20

1. Mrs. Garcia buys 2 flexible gates and 1 extension on sale.
   How much does she spend?

   Estimate?
   Exact answer?

2. An animal shelter has a discount coupon for $193 off a large purchase
   at the dog supply store. The shelter buys 113 medium dog collars with
   names and uses the discount coupon. What will be the final price?

   Estimate?
   Exact answer?

3. Emma bought a flexible gate for a room that is 8 feet wide.
   The gate is too short for her space. How many inches short is it?
   There are 12 inches in 1 foot.

   Estimate?
   Exact answer?

© K12 Inc. All rights reserved.

LEARN

Estimate to Predict and Verify (B)

Predict, Solve, and Verify Answers

Estimate to predict the answer. Then solve. Write the estimate and the exact answer.

1. The Arden family has 3 German shepherd dogs. Daisy weighs 88 pounds, Lucky weighs 106 pounds, and Otto weighs 93 pounds. How much do the 3 dogs weigh altogether?

2. A science magazine reported that a giant freshwater catfish can weigh 644 pounds. Ethan says that the largest fish he ever caught was 7 pounds. How many times heavier was the giant catfish?

3. Andy's Art Store has 321 tubes of oil paint. If 106 tubes cost $5 each and the rest cost $3 each, how much will the store take in by selling all of them?

4. Tia's grandmother lives 2,956 miles away. Tia has driven 2,458 miles so far. How much farther does Tia have to drive to get to her grandmother's house?

Choose the answer.

5. Abigail collects horse figures, horse key chains, and other horse items. She has 1,922 horse items in her collection. She decides to give away part of her collection. If she gives away 473 horse items, how many will Abigail still have?

   Which estimate could you use to verify that 1,449 is a reasonable answer to this problem?

   A. $2,200 - 400$

   B. $1,500 - 500$

   C. $2,000 - 500$

   D. $2,200 - 500$

© K12 Inc. All rights reserved.

TRY IT

Use Simpler Problems to Solve Harder Ones

Use a Simpler Problem

The way you go about solving a simple story problem can help you to solve one that is similar but more complex. Problem 2 of these Worked Examples is harder than Problem 1, but both problems ask a similar question and the 4-step plan and strategy for solving them is the same.

PROBLEM 1 Sofia is an arts and crafts counselor at a summer day camp. She has 448 loose crayons to sort into boxes with 8 crayons in each box. How many full boxes of crayons will she have?

SOLUTION

UNDERSTAND THE PROBLEM You need to separate 448 crayons into 8 equal groups.

DEVISE A PLAN To solve the problem, you can write a division number sentence: $448 \div 8 = ?$

CARRY OUT THE PLAN

$$\begin{array}{r} 56 \\ 8\overline{)448} \\ -400 \\ \hline 48 \\ -48 \\ \hline 0 \end{array}$$

← Estimate how many groups of 8 are in 448. Since 50×8 is 400, place a 5 in the quotient above the tens place in the dividend.

← Then multiply 50×8 and write 400.

← Next subtract $448 - 400$ to get 48. $48 \div 8$ is 6.

Place the 6 in the quotient above the ones place in the dividend.

Multiply 6×8 and write 48.

Subtract $48 - 48 = 0$. There is no remainder.

LOOK BACK Make sure you've answered the question that was asked. Since 56 is close to the estimate of 50, then the answer makes sense.

ANSWER Sofia will have 56 full boxes of crayons.

© K12 Inc. All rights reserved.

LEARN

PROBLEM 2 Sofia has 1,113 large beads to sort. She needs to place 21 beads in each container. How many containers will she need?

SOLUTION

UNDERSTAND THE PROBLEM You need to separate 1,113 beads into equal groups of 21.

DEVISE A PLAN Use the same strategy that you used for Problem 1. Write a division number sentence: $1,113 \div 21 = ?$

CARRY OUT THE PLAN

$$
\begin{array}{r}
53 \\
21\overline{)1,123} \\
-1,050 \\
\hline
63 \\
-63 \\
\hline
0
\end{array}
$$

Estimate how many groups of 21 are in 1,113. Since 50×20 is 1,000, place the 5 in the quotient above the tens place in the dividend.

Then multiply 50×21 and write 1,050.

Next subtract $1,113 - 1,050$ to get 63. Estimate. Since 20×3 is 60, place the 3 in the quotient above the ones place in the dividend.

Multiply 3×21 and write 63.

Subtract $63 - 63 = 0$. There is no remainder.

LOOK BACK Make sure you've answered the question that was asked. Since 53 is close to the estimate of 50, then the answer makes sense.

ANSWER Sofia will need 53 containers.

Solve Problem 1 and explain your strategy. Then look at Problem 2 and explain why you can solve it the same way as Problem 1, and solve.

1. Mrs. Lee wants to share 85 muffins equally among 5 people.

   How many muffins will each person get?

2. Mrs. Lee wants to share 2,067 muffins among 53 people.

   How many muffins will each person get?

Solve Problem 3 and explain your strategy. Then look at Problem 4 and explain why you can solve it the same way as Problem 3, and solve.

3. Luis needs to tile a lobby area 9 feet wide and 9 feet long with large square tiles that are 3 feet long and 3 feet wide.

   How many tiles will he need?

4. Luis needs to tile a space 10 feet wide and 20 feet long. The tiles are 2 feet wide and 4 feet long.

   How many tiles will he need?

© K12 Inc. All rights reserved.

LEARN

Use Simpler Problems to Solve Harder Ones

Simple and Complex Problems

© K12 Inc. All rights reserved.

Worked Examples

To solve a complex story problem, think of a similar, but simpler, problem that you know how to solve. Then apply the same strategy you used to solve the simpler problem.

PROBLEM A potter makes 156 mugs. She wants to pack 12 mugs in each box. How many boxes does she need?

SOLUTION

UNDERSTAND THE PROBLEM You need to find out how many groups of 12 mugs are in 156 mugs.

DEVISE A PLAN Rewrite the problem with simpler numbers. Replace 156 mugs with 18 mugs in the problem. Then replace 12 mugs per box with 3 mugs. How would you solve this simpler problem? A potter makes 18 mugs. She wants to pack 3 mugs in each box. How many boxes does she need?

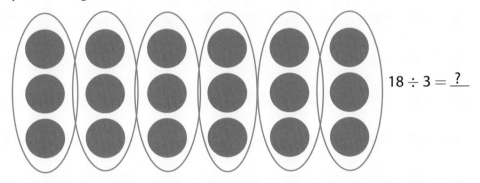

$18 \div 3 = \underline{\quad?\quad}$

Use the diagram to sketch this simpler problem. Then write the number sentence that the diagram shows.

Now look at the original problem and write a number sentence similar to the one you wrote for the simpler problem. $156 \div 12 = ?$

Solve the number sentence.

L E A R N

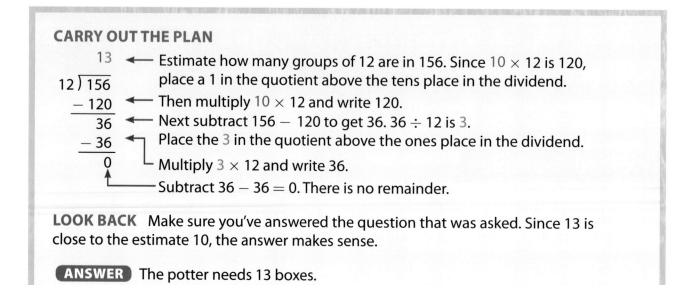

CARRY OUT THE PLAN

$$
\begin{array}{r}
13 \\
12\,\overline{)\,156} \\
-120 \\
\hline
36 \\
-36 \\
\hline
0
\end{array}
$$

← Estimate how many groups of 12 are in 156. Since 10 × 12 is 120, place a 1 in the quotient above the tens place in the dividend.

← Then multiply 10 × 12 and write 120.

← Next subtract 156 − 120 to get 36. 36 ÷ 12 is 3.

← Place the 3 in the quotient above the ones place in the dividend.

Multiply 3 × 12 and write 36.

Subtract 36 − 36 = 0. There is no remainder.

LOOK BACK   Make sure you've answered the question that was asked. Since 13 is close to the estimate 10, the answer makes sense.

ANSWER   The potter needs 13 boxes.

Read the problem. With simpler numbers, make a new problem and write a number sentence to solve. Then write a number sentence for the original problem and solve.

1. Members of the Enviro Club collected 2,272 cans. Then they were given 16 bags with 15 cans in each bag. How many cans do they have now?

    Make a simpler problem and write a number sentence.

    Members of the Enviro Club collected _?_ cans. Then they were given _?_ bags with _?_ cans in each bag. How many cans do they have now?

    _?_ + _?_ × _?_ = ?

    Solve the original problem. Remember to use the order of operations.

    2,272 ◯ 16 ◯ 15 = ?

    Answer: _?_ cans

2. A factory makes 2,272 cups. The cups will be packed into boxes with 16 cups in each box. How many boxes will the factory need?

    Make a simpler problem and write a number sentence.

    A factory makes _?_ cups. The cups will be packed into boxes with _?_ cups in each box. How many boxes will the factory need?

    _?_ ◯ _?_ = ?

    Solve the original problem.

    2,272 ◯ 16 = ?

    Answer: _?_ boxes

© K12 Inc. All rights reserved.

LEARN

3. The National Tower is 341 feet higher than the Central Tower.
   The Northwestern Tower is 243 feet taller than the National Tower.
   How much taller is the Northwestern Tower than the Central Tower?

   Make a simpler problem and write a number sentence.

   The National Tower is _?_ feet higher than the Central Tower.
   The Northwestern Tower is _?_ feet taller than the National Tower.
   How much taller is the Northwestern Tower than the Central Tower?

   _?_ ◯ _?_ = ?

   Solve the original problem.

   _?_ ◯ _?_ = ?

   Answer: _?_ feet

Solve. Then explain how you used the sketches to solve the problem.

4. Mrs. Birch is planning a charity event. She makes sketches to show the number of
   people who could sit at square tables pushed together into a rectangle.
   She sketches 1, 2, 3, and 4 square tables pushed together.

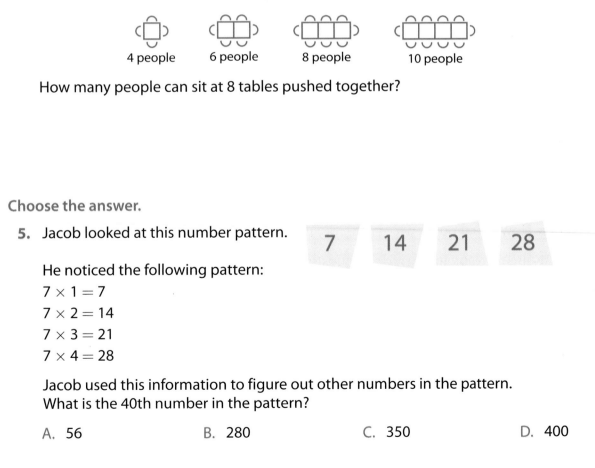

| 4 people | 6 people | 8 people | 10 people |

   How many people can sit at 8 tables pushed together?

Choose the answer.

5. Jacob looked at this number pattern.

   7   14   21   28

   He noticed the following pattern:

   $7 \times 1 = 7$
   $7 \times 2 = 14$
   $7 \times 3 = 21$
   $7 \times 4 = 28$

   Jacob used this information to figure out other numbers in the pattern.
   What is the 40th number in the pattern?

   A. 56   B. 280   C. 350   D. 400

© K12 Inc. All rights reserved.

LEARN

Represent and Explain Story Problems

More than One Strategy to Solve

Worked Examples

You can use different strategies to solve a story problem. You can decide which strategy you want to use.

PROBLEM Johnny saw some animals at a pet store. He saw 4 cats. He saw 3 times as many dogs as cats. He saw 5 fewer hamsters than dogs. How many animals did Johnny see at the pet store?

SOLUTION 1

UNDERSTAND THE PROBLEM You need to find out how many cats Johnny saw, how many dogs he saw, and how many hamsters he saw at the pet store. Then you need to find out how many animals he saw in all.

DEVISE A PLAN You can draw a diagram. Use circles to show the different types of animals. Let C stand for cat, D for dog, and H for hamster.

- Johnny saw 4 cats. Draw 4 circles and write C in each circle.
- He saw 3 times as many dogs as cats. Draw 3 groups of 4 circles and write D in each circle.
- He saw 5 fewer hamsters than dogs. Count the number of D circles and draw 5 fewer circles. Write H in each circle.

CARRY OUT THE PLAN Use the diagram. Count the total number of circles. There are 23 circles, so Johnny saw 23 animals at the pet store.

C = cat

D = dog

H = hamster

LOOK BACK Be sure you answered the question. Reread the problem to be sure you drew the diagram correctly. Count the circles again.

ANSWER Johnny saw 23 animals at the pet store.

© K12 Inc. All rights reserved.

L E A R N

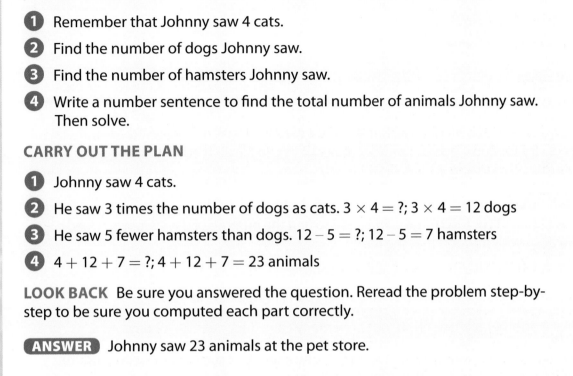

SOLUTION 2

UNDERSTAND THE PROBLEM See Solution 1.

DEVISE A PLAN This problem is a multistep problem. You need to break the problem into steps.

1 Remember that Johnny saw 4 cats.

2 Find the number of dogs Johnny saw.

3 Find the number of hamsters Johnny saw.

4 Write a number sentence to find the total number of animals Johnny saw. Then solve.

CARRY OUT THE PLAN

1 Johnny saw 4 cats.

2 He saw 3 times the number of dogs as cats. $3 \times 4 = ?$; $3 \times 4 = 12$ dogs

3 He saw 5 fewer hamsters than dogs. $12 - 5 = ?$; $12 - 5 = 7$ hamsters

4 $4 + 12 + 7 = ?$; $4 + 12 + 7 = 23$ animals

LOOK BACK Be sure you answered the question. Reread the problem step-by-step to be sure you computed each part correctly.

ANSWER Johnny saw 23 animals at the pet store.

Explain how to solve the story problem two different ways. Then solve.

1. Kerry invited 16 people to her birthday party. 6 people can sit at a long dining-room table. 4 people can sit at a square table. What is the fewest number of square tables needed so each guest will have a seat?

2. A recipe calls for 0.35 ounces of sprinkles on each dozen cookies. Lyle wants to decorate 36 cookies. How many ounces of sprinkles will Lyle need?

3. A statue of a man is 12.7 feet tall. The base that it sits on is 5.4 feet high. It traveled 345 miles to be put in place. How tall is the statue from the bottom of the base to the top of the statue's head?

© K12 Inc. All rights reserved.

L E A R N

Represent and Explain Story Problems

Same Problem, Different Ways

Worked Examples

You can make a table or draw a diagram to solve a story problem.

PROBLEM Sarah has two dogs. Prince eats 2 cans of dog food every 3 days and 1 bag of dry food in 12 days. Bucky eats 2 cans of dog food every 2 days and 2 bags of dry food in 12 days. For how many days can Sarah feed both dogs with 40 cans of dog food and 6 bags of dry food?

SOLUTION 1

UNDERSTAND THE PROBLEM You need to find the number of days Sarah can feed her two dogs with the food that she has.

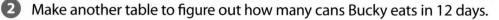

DEVISE A PLAN Use the make-a-table strategy.

❶ Make one table to figure out how many cans Prince eats in 12 days.

❷ Make another table to figure out how many cans Bucky eats in 12 days.

❸ Compare the total amount of food the dogs eat in 12 days to the total amount of food that Sarah has. Then decide how many days the food will last.

CARRY OUT THE PLAN

❶

Prince's Food				
Days	3	6	9	12
Cans	2	4	6	8

Prince eats 8 cans and 1 bag of food in 12 days.

❷

Bucky's Food						
Days	2	4	6	8	10	12
Cans	2	4	6	8	10	12

Bucky eats 12 cans and 2 bags of food in 12 days.

© K12 Inc. All rights reserved.

L E A R N

3 They eat $8 + 12 = 20$ cans of food and $1 + 2 = 3$ bags of food in 12 days. Since 40 cans of food $= 2 \times 20$ cans and 6 bags of food $= 2 \times 3$ bags, then Sarah will have enough food for 2×12 days $= 24$ days.

LOOK BACK Does 24 days answer the question? Yes, because you need to find for how many days Sarah can feed her dog with 40 cans and 6 bags. That's exactly how much food the dogs will eat in 24 days.

SOLUTION 2

UNDERSTAND THE PROBLEM See Solution 1.

DEVISE A PLAN Use the draw-a-diagram strategy.

1 Draw a diagram to find how many cans of food the dogs eat in 12 days.

2 Draw another diagram to find how many bags of food the dogs eat in 12 days.

3 Compare the total amount of food the dogs eat in 12 days to the total amount of food that Sarah has.

CARRY OUT THE PLAN

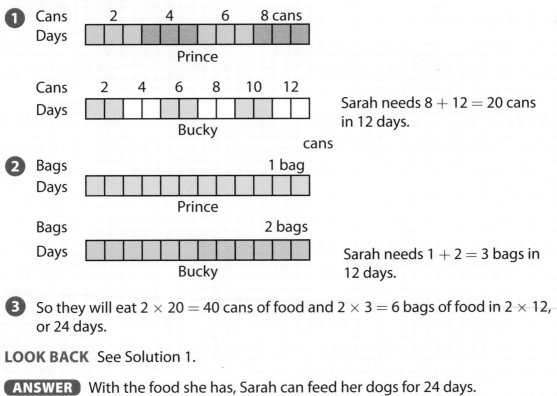

Sarah needs $8 + 12 = 20$ cans in 12 days.

Sarah needs $1 + 2 = 3$ bags in 12 days.

3 So they will eat $2 \times 20 = 40$ cans of food and $2 \times 3 = 6$ bags of food in 2×12, or 24 days.

LOOK BACK See Solution 1.

ANSWER With the food she has, Sarah can feed her dogs for 24 days.

© K12 Inc. All rights reserved.

L E A R N

Solve the problem two different ways.

1. Alex has $1.40 in his pocket. He has 11 coins in all. He has 3 quarters and a combination of dimes and nickels.

   How many dimes does Alex have?

   How many nickels does Alex have?

2. A novelty store has 350 toy figures of popular music stars. Each bin holds 25 figures.

   How many bins will hold all 350 figures?

3. The Antonini family bought hot dog rolls in packages of 10 and hot dogs in packages of 6. Each adult at the picnic eats 3 hot dogs and 3 hot dog rolls.

   How many packages of rolls and hot dogs will the family have to buy to feed 20 adults?

© K12 Inc. All rights reserved.

LEARN

Represent and Explain Story Problems

Identify Two Strategies

Solve two ways. Explain the strategies.

1. Bryson bought some pencils, pens, and markers at the office supply store. He bought 3 times as many pencils as pens. He bought 5 more markers than pens. He bought 6 pens. How many items did Bryson buy at the office supply store?

Choose the two strategies that can be used to solve the problem.

2. Anna had some flowers. She arranged 18 flowers in each of 8 vases. She had 11 flowers left over. How many flowers did she have to start?

   A. Guess and test. Try starting with 100 flowers. Subtract 21 repeatedly until the difference is less than 21. Count the number of times you subtracted. If you did not subtract 21 eight times and end up with 11 flowers left over, 100 is not right. Adjust the number and repeat.

   B. Write a number sentence and solve.
      $8 \times 18 + 11 = \underline{\ ?\ }$

   C. Draw a picture. Sketch 8 groups of 18, then 11 more, and count them all.

3. Volunteers are setting up benches for an exhibition at a town fair. They will use long benches that can seat 12 people each and short benches that can seat 5 people each. What is the fewest number of short benches that volunteers can set up so that 58 people can have seats?

   A. Draw a picture. Draw 58 dots. Circle as many groups of 12 as you can. Then circle as many groups of 5 as you can from the dots that are not already circled. Count the number of groups of 5.

   B. Work backward. Begin with 58. Subtract 12 repeatedly until the difference is less than 12. Then subtract 5 until the difference is less than 5. Count the number of 5s you subtracted.

   C. Write number sentences and solve.
      $5 \times 12 = 60$ and $60 - 58 = \underline{\ ?\ }$

   D. Explain that 5 times 10 equals 50, so you need 10 short benches.

© K12 Inc. All rights reserved.

T R Y   I T

4. A frozen yogurt shop owner sold vanilla, chocolate, and banana yogurt pops. In one hour, the owner sold one more banana pop than chocolate pops. She sold twice as many vanilla pops as banana pops. If the owner sold 7 chocolate pops, how many total pops did she sell in one hour?

A. Work backward. She sold 7 chocolate pops, so multiply 7 by 2 and add 1.

B. Draw a diagram. Draw 7 chocolate pops. Then draw 1 more banana pop than chocolate pops, or 8 banana pops. Then draw two times as many vanilla pops as banana pops, or 16 vanilla pops. Count all the yogurt pops to find the total.

C. Use logical thinking. There were 7 chocolate pops. Add 1 to get 8 because one more banana than chocolate pops was sold. Double the 8 to get 16 because twice as many vanilla as banana pops were sold. Then add $7 + 8 + 16$.

D. Write a number sentence and solve.
$2 \times 7 + 1 = \underline{\ ?\ }$

© K12 Inc. All rights reserved.

State Solutions Clearly (A)
Make-a-Table Strategy

Worked Examples

You can make a table to organize the data in a story problem.

PROBLEM Layla recorded the daily high and low temperatures in her city for five days: Highs: Mon. 81°, Tues. 82°, Wed. 80°, Thurs. 80°, Fri. 79°; Lows: Mon. 63°, Tues. 65°, Wed. 60°, Thurs. 67°, Fri. 62°. On which day was the difference between the high and low temperatures the greatest? Solve and explain how you solved the problem.

SOLUTION

UNDERSTAND THE PROBLEM To see which day of the week had the greatest difference in temperatures, find the difference between the high and low temperatures of each day.

DEVISE A PLAN Use the make-a-table strategy. Arrange the data by days of the week so that the lows can easily be subtracted from the highs. Subtract. Identify the day with the greatest difference. Then explain how you solved the problem.

CARRY OUT THE PLAN

	Mon.	Tues.	Wed.	Thurs.	Fri.
High Temp.	81°	82°	80°	80°	79°
Low Temp.	63°	65°	60°	67°	62°
Difference	18°	17°	20°	13°	17°

The greatest difference was 20° and occurred on Wednesday.

LOOK BACK Be sure the data on the table matches the data in the problem. Check your subtraction and compare the differences again.

ANSWER The greatest difference occurred on Wednesday. To solve the problem, subtract each day's low temperature from its high temperature, find the greatest difference, and identify the day it occurred.

© K12 Inc. All rights reserved.

L E A R N

Complete the table to solve the problem.

1. The city of Twin Lakes has a weeklong town carnival each year. Mr. Buckle recorded the number of adult tickets and child tickets that were sold each day.

Adult tickets:
Monday   318
Tuesday   425
Wednesday 376
Thursday   404
Friday   418
Saturday   514
Sunday   511

Child tickets:
Monday   375
Tuesday   350
Wednesday 480
Thursday   270
Friday   500
Saturday   320
Sunday   285

On which day did the carnival sell the most tickets?

How many more tickets were sold on Wednesday than on Tuesday?

Explain how you solved the problem.

	Monday	Tuesday	Wednesday	Thursday	Friday	Saturday	Sunday
Adult tickets	?	?	?	?	?	?	?
Child tickets	?	?	?	?	?	?	?
Total	?	?	?	?	?	?	?

2. Ashley has 1 dime, 5 nickels, and 20 pennies. She found six ways to use some of her coins to show 18¢. Use the table to find the six ways that Ashley can use some of her coins to show 18¢.

Then explain how you solved the problem.

Number of Dimes	Number of Nickels	Number of Pennies	Total Value
?	?	?	18¢
?	?	?	18¢
?	?	?	18¢
?	?	?	18¢
?	?	?	18¢
?	?	?	18¢

© K12 Inc. All rights reserved.

Read the problem and follow the directions.

3. Write a story problem that uses the data in the table. Then solve the problem and explain how you solved it.

	Art Club	Music Club	Dance Club	Sport Club	Chess Club
Money raised	$675	$715	$682	$764	$520
Expenses	$411	$430	$459	$582	$322
?	?	?	?	?	?

© K12 Inc. All rights reserved.

LEARN

State Solutions Clearly (A)

Solve and Explain

Explain how to solve the problem, and then solve.

1. Tickets for the zoo cost $15 each for adult tickets and $9 each for child tickets. Mrs. Porter bought 8 tickets. She spent a total of $90. How many of each type of ticket did Mrs. Porter buy?

2. Zeke is saving money to buy a new bike. The bike costs $218. He starts with $42 in his savings account. Each week he deposits $15. How many weeks will it take for Zeke to save enough to buy the bike?

Choose the explanation that best describes how to solve the problem.

3. Elena ran 20 miles every week for 5 weeks. She ran 25 miles the sixth week and 33 miles the seventh week. How far did Elena run in 7 weeks?

   A. **Write a number sentence.** $20 + 5 + 25 + 6 + 33 + 7 = \underline{\ ?\ }$
   Elena ran 96 miles.

   B. **Break up the problem into smaller problems.** Multiply 20 by 5 to get 100 miles in 5 weeks. Add 25 miles and 33 miles to figure out how many miles she ran in the sixth and seventh weeks. Add $100 + 58$ together. Elena ran 158 miles.

   C. **Work backward.** Elena ran 20 miles in 5 weeks. That means she ran 4 miles in 1 week. Add 4 miles to 25 and 33. Elena ran 62 miles.

   D. **Make a table.** Elena ran 33 miles.

Week	1	2	3	4	5	6	7
Miles	20	20	20	20	20	25	33

© K12 Inc. All rights reserved.

TRY IT

4. The zoo has 32 lizards in the enclosure. 10 of the lizards are yellow, and 6 of the lizards are red. Half of the remaining lizards are green. How many lizards are green?

   A. **Work backward.** Start with the original number of lizards. Divide by 2 as half of the lizards are green, and then subtract 10 and 6.

   B. **Guess and test.** Guess that there are 10 green lizards. Half of 10 is 5. Add 10 and add 6 to get 21. That is fewer than the number of lizards in the zoo, so try again with another number. Guess that there are 40 green lizards. Half of 40 is 20. Add 10 and add 6 to get 36. That is more than the number of lizards in the zoo, so try again with another number. Guess that there are 32 green lizards. Half of 32 is 16. Add 10 and add 6 to get 32.

   C. **Write a number sentence.** $(32 - 10 - 6) \times 2 = \underline{?}$

   D. **Make a diagram.** Draw 32 dots to represent the 32 lizards. Cross out 10 of them for the yellow lizards and 6 of them for the red lizards. Take the remaining 16 dots and cross out half of them (8 dots). The number of dots remaining is the number of green lizards in the zoo.

5. Carl spent 45 minutes on his French homework, and 1 hour on his math homework. He talked on the phone for 15 minutes and then drove to his tennis practice. The drive took 20 minutes. His tennis practice started at 5:30 p.m. What time did Carl start his French homework?

   A. **Guess and test.** Start at 2:00, and add 45 minutes. The time is now 2:45. Add 1 hour. The time is now 3:45. Add 15 minutes. The time is now 4:00. Add 20 minutes. Carl started his French homework at 4:20.

   B. **Write a number sentence.** $530 - (45 + 1 + 15 + 20) = \underline{?}$
      Carl started his French homework at 4:49.

   C. **Make a diagram.** Draw a clock. First show the minute hand starting at 12. Draw another clock. Add 45 minutes. The minute hand now points to the 9. Draw another clock. Add 1 hour. The minute hand points to the 9. Draw another clock. Add 15 minutes. The minute hand now points to the 12. Draw another clock. Add 20 minutes. The minute hand now points to the 5. Carl started his French homework at 25 minutes after the hour.

   D. **Work backward.** Start at 5:30, and subtract 20 minutes; he left for tennis practice at 5:10. Subtract 15 minutes; he started talking on the phone at 4:55. Subtract 1 hour; he started math homework at 3:55. Subtract 45 minutes. Carl started his French homework at 3:10.

© K12 Inc. All rights reserved.

T R Y   I T

6. Susie bought a balloon and a card to give to her grandfather every month. Each balloon cost $7 and each card cost $2. How much money did Susie spend in 6 months?

   A. **Make a table.** Susie spent $54.

Month	1	2	3	4	5	6
Total Cost	$9	$18	$27	$36	$45	$54

   B. **Draw a picture.** Draw 7 circles and write $7 in each one. Draw 2 circles and write $2 in each one. Add up the amounts in the circles. Susie spent $53.

   C. **Use objects to model the problem.** Take 7 blocks and 2 blocks and put them together to get 9 blocks. Susie spent $9 altogether.

   D. **Break the problem into steps.** Multiply the cost of flowers by the cost of the card ($7 × $2). Multiply the cost by the number of months ($14 × $6). Susie spent $84.

7. Rachael rode her bike 15 miles every week for 5 weeks. She rode her bike 18 miles the sixth week and 19 miles the seventh week. How far did Rachael ride her bike in 7 weeks?

   A. Add 15 and 5 and 18 and 6 and 19 and 7.

   B. Add 15 and 5. Then add 18 and 19. Then add the two sums together.

   C. Multiply 15 × 5. Then add 18 and 19 to the product.

   D. Divide 15 by 5. Then add 18 and 19 to the quotient.

8. Six boys want to go to the movies and then go for pizza. They have a total of $100. The movie tickets cost $10 each. How much money will the boys have left to buy pizza?

   A. Add 6 and 100 and 10.

   B. Divide 100 by 6. Then add 10 to the quotient.

   C. Multiply 10 × 6. Then subtract the product from 100.

   D. Add 10 and 6. Then multiply the sum by 100.

9. Over summer vacation, Alice read 3 books a week for the first 3 weeks and then 2 books a week for the last 3 weeks. How many books did Alice read?

   A. Add 3 and 3 and 2 and 3.

   B. Add 3 and 2. Multiply the sum by 2.

   C. Multiply 3 × 3. Then multiply 2 × 3. Then add the two products.

   D. Add 3 and 3. Then divide the sum by 3.

TRY IT

© K12 Inc. All rights reserved.

10. The toy factory makes 120 toy cars in a day. Each day 10 of the cars are rejected because they have flaws in the paint. How many flawless cars can the toy factory make in 400 days?

   A. Add 120 and 10 and 400.

   B. Multiply 120 × 10. Subtract the product from 400.

   C. Divide 120 by 10. Add the quotient to 400.

   D. Subtract 10 from 120. Multiply the difference by 400.

Choose the explanation that best describes the answer to the problem.

11. A sports club can have a maximum of 15 people in each yoga class. How many classes will the club need if 87 people sign up for yoga?

   A. Divide 87 by 15. The answer is 5 with 12 left over. So the club will need 5 classes.

   B. Multiply 87 by 15. The answer is 1,218. So the club will need 1,218 classes.

   C. Divide 87 by 15. The answer is 5 with 12 left over. So the club will need 6 classes.

   D. Multiply 87 by 15. The answer is 1,305. So the club will need 1,305 classes.

12. The farmworkers put 12 eggs in each box. They boxed 3,364 eggs in one month. How many complete boxes did the workers fill?

   A. Divide 3,364 by 12. The answer is 280 with 4 left over. So the farmworkers can fill 281 boxes.

   B. Divide 3,364 by 12. The answer is 280 with 4 left over. So the farmworkers can fill 280 boxes.

   C. Divide 3,364 by 12. The answer is 28 with 4 left over. So the farmworkers can fill 29 boxes.

   D. Divide 3,364 by 12. The answer is 276 with 5 left over. So the farmworkers can fill 277 boxes.

© K12 Inc. All rights reserved.

TRY IT

State Solutions Clearly (B)
Work-Backward Strategy

Worked Examples

You can use the work-backward strategy to solve a story problem.

PROBLEM Layla has an eye appointment at 9:30 a.m. tomorrow. She needs to be there 15 minutes early to fill out forms. It takes her 30 minutes to get ready in the morning and she needs to allow 25 minutes to get to the eye doctor's office from home. At what time should Layla start getting ready tomorrow?

Solve. Then explain how you solved the problem

SOLUTION

UNDERSTAND THE PROBLEM The ending time is given (9:30 a.m.) and the starting time needs to be found. (The starting time is when Layla needs to start getting ready.)

DEVISE A PLAN Work backward. Start at the time Layla must be at the doctor's office. Then move back the number of minutes it takes each event to happen to find what time she should start getting ready.

CARRY OUT THE PLAN Start at the ending time and move back by subtracting the minutes Layla will spend on each event.

start here
↓

8:20 a.m. ← minus 30 min ← 8:50 a.m. ← minus 25 min ← 9:15 a.m. ← minus 15 min ← 9:30 a.m.

So 8:20 a.m. is the time Layla should start getting ready.

LOOK BACK To be sure the answer makes sense, write the answer, 8:20 a.m., on the far left. Add the minutes for each event, moving to the right. Since the result is 9:30 a.m., then the answer of 8:20 a.m. is correct.

8:20 a.m. → plus 30 min → 8:50 a.m. → plus 25 min → 9:15 a.m. → plus 15 min → 9:30 a.m.

ANSWER Layla should start getting ready at 8:20 a.m. To solve the problem, you start at the ending time. You subtract the minutes Layla spent on each event, recording the time before each event. The final time you record is the time Layla should start getting ready.

© K12 Inc. All rights reserved.

L E A R N

Solve. Then explain how you solved the problem.

1. Carl started with some money in his savings account. He withdrew $30, then deposited $75. Next he deposited $40 and withdrew $50. Now he has $148. How much money did Carl start with in his savings account?

2. Some people were at the museum when it opened at 10:00 a.m. By noon, 98 people had entered the museum and 32 people had left. From noon until 8:00 p.m., 128 more people arrived and 79 left. At 8:00 p.m., 200 people remained in the museum. How many people were at the museum when it opened?

Read the problem and follow the directions.

3. Write a 3- or 4-sentence story problem that uses the information in the table. Then work backward to solve the problem.

Movie title	Start time	Length of movie
Shark Attack!	1:30 p.m., 4:30 p.m., 7:00 p.m.	109 minutes
Friends in Space	1:15 p.m., 3:50 p.m., 6:30 p.m.	117 minutes
Playground Capers	1:25 p.m., 4:45 p.m., 7:15 p.m.	110 minutes
Mystery Mission	1:20 p.m., 4:15 p.m., 6:45 p.m.	98 minutes

© K12 Inc. All rights reserved.

LEARN

Problem-Solving Strategies

Select the Strategy

● ● ●

Worked Examples

For each story problem, some problem-solving strategies are more helpful than others. Before you devise a plan, you need to look for strategies that will help you correctly solve the problem. You also need to identify strategies that will not help you correctly solve the problem.

PROBLEM Which strategy would **not** correctly solve this story problem?

Trent wants to get a cell phone. The phone costs $50. Cell phone service costs $42 a month. How much money does Trent need to get a cell phone and service for 6 months?

A. Make a table.

Month	1	2	3	4	5	6
Total Cost	$92	$134	$176	$218	$260	?

B. Make a line graph.

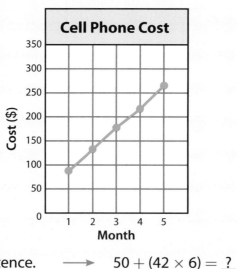

C. Write a number sentence. ⟶ $50 + (42 \times 6) = \underline{\ ?\ }$

D. Make a model. ⟶ Take 42 pieces of play money.
Divide the money into 6 equal groups.
Add $50 to each group.

SOLUTION

UNDERSTAND THE PROBLEM You need to find out which strategy would **not** correctly solve this story problem.

© K12 Inc. All rights reserved.

DEVISE A PLAN Look at each answer choice and ask yourself, "Will this strategy correctly solve this story problem? Why or why not?" The answer choice that will **not** correctly solve this story problem is the correct answer.

CARRY OUT THE PLAN
- **Answer choice A.** Yes. The table shows the amount Trent would spend each month and includes the cost of the phone and the monthly service fee. If you complete the table, you will find the amount spent in 6 months.
- **Answer choice B.** Yes. The graph shows a linear relationship because the same amount, or $42, is spent each month after the first month. If you extend the straight line with a straightedge, you will find the amount that will be spent in 6 months.
- **Answer choice C.** Yes. The monthly fee is $42, so the monthly fee for 6 months is $42 × 6. Add this to the cost of the cell phone ($50) to get the equation $50 + (42 \times 6) = \underline{?}$. If you solve this number sentence, you will find the amount that will be spent in 6 months.
- **Answer choice D.** No. This model shows division instead of multiplication. It would **not** correctly solve this problem, so it is the correct answer choice.

LOOK BACK Make sure you've answered the question that was asked. Have you found the answer choice that will **not** correctly solve this story problem?

ANSWER Answer choice D is the correct answer to the question, "Which strategy does **not** correctly solve this story problem?"

Choose the strategy that would **not** correctly solve the problem.

1. Samantha notices that it is 2:15 p.m. now. Her friend Shelly called her 30 minutes ago. At that time, Shelly told Samantha that she had left home in another city 2 hours and 45 minutes earlier to come visit. What time did Shelly leave home?

   A. **Work backward.** The end time is 2:15 p.m. Subtract (go back) 30 minutes. Then subtract (go back) 2 hours and 45 minutes to find the start time.

   B. **Look for a pattern.**
   2 hours 15 minutes
   0 minutes
   2 hours 45 minutes

   C. **Guess and test.** Guess a time before 2:15 and then check if it works with the information in the problem. Add 2 hours 45 minutes to the time and then add another 30 minutes. If the end time is 2:15 p.m., the start time is correct.

   D. **Make a model.** Use or draw a clock to model the problem. Set the time to 2:15. Then move the minute hand back half a turn to show 30 minutes. This is the time of the phone call. Then move the minute hand back again to show 45 minutes. Move the hour hand back 2 numbers to show the 2 hours. The time shown is the start time.

© K12 Inc. All rights reserved.

LEARN

Choose the strategy that would not correctly solve the problem.

2. Helen had some pocket money. Her sister had $6 and Helen had twice as much money as her sister. Helen spent $2 at the post office and $3 at the newspaper store. How much money did Helen have left?

    A. **Use objects to model the problem.** Take 6 pieces of play money. Take away 2 pieces and then take away 3 pieces.

    B. **Draw a diagram.** Draw 6 dots to represent how much money Helen's sister has. Draw 12 dots to show how much money Helen has. Cross out 2 of Helen's dots to represent the money she spent at the post office. Cross out 3 of Helen's dots to represent the money she spent at the newspaper store. Circle the remaining dots in Helen's group.

    C. **Use logical reasoning.** Multiply 6 by 2 to figure out how much money Helen has to begin with. The answer is 12. Subtract 2 from 12 for the money Helen spent at the post office. The answer is 10. Subtract 3 from 10 for the money Helen spent at the newspaper store.

    D. **Translate into a number sentence.** $(6 \times 2) - (3 + 2) = \underline{?}$

Choose the strategy that would correctly solve the story problem.

3. A square game board has 4 small squares in each row and 4 small squares in each column. How would you shade the small squares so that each row and each column has 2 and only 2 small squares shaded?

    A. **Use logical reasoning.** If the square game board has 4 squares in each row and column, then to have 2 squares shaded in each row and column, shade 1 square in each row and 1 square in each column.

    B. **Draw a diagram.** On grid paper, draw a square that is 4 squares wide and 4 squares long. Shade 2 squares in each row. Check if the diagram shows 2 and only 2 small squares shaded in each column. Repeat if it does not. Continue until you find a combination that matches the information in the problem.

    C. **Write a number sentence.** $(4 \times 4) \div 2 = \underline{?}$

© K12 Inc. All rights reserved.

LEARN

Problem-Solving Strategies

Different Strategies

Choose the strategy that would **not** correctly solve the problem.

1. Susie bought a sandwich and an iced tea each day at work.
   Each sandwich cost $4 and each iced tea cost $2. How much money did
   Susie spend in 7 days?

   A. **Write a number sentence.**
      $(7 \times 4) + (7 \times 2) = \underline{\ ?\ }$

   B. **Make a coordinate graph.**

   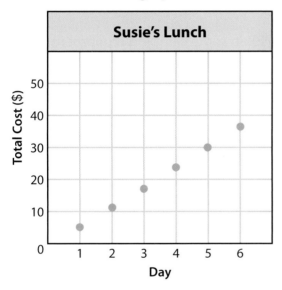

   C. **Make a table.**

   Susie's Lunch

Day	1	2	3	4	5	6	7
Total Cost ($)	$6	$12	$18	$24	$30	$36	?

   D. **Use objects to model the problem.** Take 4 pieces of play money.
      Divide the money into 2 equal groups. Add $7 to each group.

© K12 Inc. All rights reserved.

TRY IT

2. There are 21 children at the summer camp. There are 2 times as many boys as girls. How many boys are there at the summer camp?

   A. **Draw a diagram.** Draw 21 dots. Divide the group into 3 equal groups. Draw a rectangle around 2 of the groups. Count the number of dots inside the rectangle.

   B. **Use logical reasoning.** To find out how many children at the summer camp are boys, divide the total number into 3 groups, which gives 7 in each group. As there are twice as many boys as girls, multiply 7 by 2 to get 14.

   C. **Write a number sentence.**
      $(21 \div 3) \times 2 = \underline{\ ?\ }$

   D. **Work backward.** There are 21 children at the camp. There are twice as many boys as girls, so divide by 2 to find out how many boys are at the summer camp.

3. Annie made $460 one summer. She spent $40 on some camping equipment, she spent twice as much on a new bicycle, and she spent half of what was left on her vacation. How much money did Annie spend on her vacation?

   A. **Use logical reasoning.** Start with $460. Subtract $40 to get $420. Multiply $40 by 2 to get the amount spent on the bicycle. Subtract $80 from $420 to get $340. Divide $340 by 2 to get the amount Annie spent on her vacation.

   B. **Draw a diagram.** Draw 46 tallies, one for each $10 Annie earned. Cross out 4 tallies for the $40 she spent on camping equipment. Cross out 8 tallies for the $80 spent on the bicycle. Circle half of the remaining tallies and multiply the number by $10.

   C. **Write a number sentence.**
      $\$460 - (\$40 + \$40 \times 2) = \$340$
      $\$340 \div 2 = \underline{\ ?\ }$

   D. **Guess and test.** Guess that Annie spent $100 on her vacation. Add $40 + $80 to $100 to get $220. Then multiply by 2.

© K12 Inc. All rights reserved.

TRY IT

4. Victor is raising money for charity. He raises $4 for each mile he runs and $2 for each mile he rides his bike. How much money will Victor raise if he runs for 5 miles and rides his bike for 10 miles?

   A. **Use logical reasoning.**

      Step 1: Multiply $4 by 5 to figure out how much money Victor makes from running.

      Step 2: Then multiply $2 by 10 to figure out how much money Victor makes from riding his bike.

      Step 3: Add the two products together.

   B. **Wrtie a number sentence.**

      $(4 \times 5) + (2 \times 10) = \underline{\ ?\ }$

   C. **Use objects to model the problem.** Use play money.

      Make 5 groups of $4. Make 10 groups of $2. Add up the money.

   D. **Draw a diagram.** Draw 2 circles. In one write $4 and in the other write $2. Draw a large circle around both of them to show how much money Victor makes.

5. Kelly invited 120 people to the wedding. 30 of them were her family members. 25 of them were her husband's family members, and the rest were friends of the family. How many friends of the family were invited to the wedding?

   A. **Write a number sentence.**

      $120 - (30 + 25) = \underline{\ ?\ }$

   B. **Use logical reasoning.** Add together the number of Kelly's family (30) and the number of her husband's family (25) to find the total number of family members. Subtract this from 120 (the number of people invited) to find the number of family friends invited.

   C. **Work backward.** Start with 120. Subtract 30 (the number of people from Kelly's family). Then subtract 25 (the number of people from her husband's family). The number left is the number of family friends who were invited.

   D. **Draw a diagram.** Draw 12 tallies, each one representing 10 guests. Cross out 3 tallies and then cross out 2 tallies. Multiply the number of tallies left by 10.

© K12 Inc. All rights reserved.

TRY IT

6. Charlotte had some pineapples to sell at the fruit stand. Her friend gave her another 4 pineapples to sell. Charlotte sold 12 pineapples. Charlotte has 10 pineapples left over. How many pineapples did Charlotte have to begin with?

A. **Draw a diagram.** Draw 10 pineapples. Draw 12 pineapples for the pineapples that were sold, and cross out 4 pineapples for the ones Charlotte's friend gave her. Count how many are left over to find the number Charlotte had to begin with.

B. **Work backward.** Start with the number of pineapples that Charlotte has left (10). Add the pineapples that were sold (12) and take away the pineapples that Charlotte's friend gave her (4).

C. **Use logical reasoning.** Charlotte had 10 pineapples left. Her friend gave her 4, so add 4. She sold 12, so subtract 12.

D. **Write a number sentence.**
$10 + 12 - 4 = \underline{\ ?\ }$

© K12 Inc. All rights reserved.

TRY IT

Estimated and Exact Answers

Determine Accuracy and Solve

Worked Examples

Before you solve a story problem, it's helpful to decide whether the answer should be exact or approximate.

PROBLEM A website for children receives an average of 985 visits per hour from 8 a.m. to 8 p.m. On any given day, how many visits will the website likely receive between 8 a.m. and 8 p.m.?

Does the problem need an approximate or exact answer? Why?
What is the answer?

SOLUTION

UNDERSTAND THE PROBLEM The question asks how many visits the website will *likely* receive between 8 a.m. and 8 p.m. The word *likely* tells you that you can estimate, or find an approximate answer.

DEVISE A PLAN To solve, round 985 to the nearest thousand. Then multiply the rounded number by 12, the number of hours between 8 a.m. and 8 p.m.

CARRY OUT THE PLAN 985 rounded to the nearest thousand is 1,000.
$1,000 \times 12 = 12,000$

LOOK BACK The answer 12,000 makes sense because the website receives almost 1,000 visits each hour over 12 hours.

ANSWER The problem needs an approximate answer because the question asks how many visits the website will *likely* receive. The website will likely receive about 12,000 visits between 8 a.m. and 8 p.m.

© K12 Inc. All rights reserved.

L E A R N

Read the problem and answer the questions.

1. In a balloon toss game, each team had 3 pairs of players. The judges added the longest distance that each pair of players tossed a balloon without breaking it. Look at the distances for each team in the chart. Which team had the highest sum of distances and won the balloon toss game?

   Does the problem need an approximate or exact answer? Why? What is the answer?

Maximum Distance (in feet)		
	Red Team	Blue Team
Pair 1	10.29	13.48
Pair 2	13.05	8.12
Pair 3	11.33	10.91

2. Hannah polled her friends to see how many minutes they listen to music each day. Then she made a table showing the results. She wanted to know how many of her friends listen to music for at least 90 minutes every day. So she analyzed the results to find the answer: 54 friends listen to music for 90 minutes or more each day.

Number of minutes	Less than 30	30 to 59	60 to 89	90 to 119	120 to 149	150 to 179	180 or more
Number of friends	15	27	29	21	18	12	3

   Is Hannah's answer an exact or approximate number?
   What did Hannah find out?

3. Josh wants to build a wooden bench that is 20.5 feet long. He has 3 lengths of board: 4.83 feet, 7.62 feet, and 9.87 feet. Does he have enough board to build the bench?

   Should Josh find an approximate or an exact answer? Why or why not? What is the answer?

© K12 Inc. All rights reserved.

Estimated and Exact Answers

Explain Accuracy and Solve

Read the problem and follow the directions.

1. The National Park Service reported that 273,488,751 people visited U.S. national parks in a recent year. It is expected that an additional 100,000 will visit the parks next year. About how many people will visit the parks next year? (Express your answer to the nearest hundred thousand.)

2. Joan is at a restaurant and wants to order soup, a sandwich, and a glass of milk. She is trying to decide if she has enough money to order a cup of soup or a bowl of soup. A cup of soup costs $2.99 and a bowl of soup costs $4.49. A sandwich costs $4.95 and a glass of milk costs $1.98. Joan has $10.00.

   Explain one reason why Joan would want to simply estimate the cost of her meal.

   Explain one reason why Joan would want to figure out the exact cost of the meal.

Choose the answer.

3. Tony wants to buy some acrylic paint. He needs 40 mL of bright red, 65 mL of cobalt blue, and 50 mL of olive green. Each bottle holds 59 mL of paint.

   Which statement is correct?

   A. Tony should add all the amounts together and buy exactly 155 mL of paint, or 2.6 bottles of paint.

   B. Tony must calculate each amount separately and buy 1 bottle of bright red paint, 2 bottles of cobalt blue paint, and 1 bottle of olive green paint.

   C. Tony can round each number to the nearest 50 and add to find that he needs 150 mL of paint, or 2.5 bottles.

© K12 Inc. All rights reserved.

TRY IT

4. Sammie wants to buy a tube of gold oil paint that costs $8.79, a tube of bright red that costs $6.59, and a large tube of zinc white that costs $21.61. Sammie has $38.00.

   Which **two** statements are correct?

   A. If Sammie rounds the costs to the nearest dollar, she will know whether the cashier has given her the correct amount of change.

   B. If Sammie rounds the costs to the nearest dollar, she can estimate whether she has enough money to buy the paint.

   C. If Sammie calculates exactly how much the paint costs, she will know whether the cashier is charging her the correct amount of money.

5. A plumber is installing a bathroom. The plans call for seven pieces of pipe to be cut 4.6 in. long and three pieces of pipe to be cut 5.1 in. long.

   Which statement is correct?

   A. The plumber can cut 10 pieces of pipe exactly 5 in. long.

   B. The plumber should cut the pieces to the exact measurements given.

   C. The plumber can cut each piece of pipe about 5 in. long.

6. Janie is making strawberry pies. She needs 5 cups of strawberries for each pie.

   Which statement is correct?

   A. It is impossible to measure exactly 5 cups of strawberries, so Janie should put the strawberries in the blender and then measure 5 cups.

   B. Janie should cut the strawberries into very tiny pieces so that she can use exactly 5 cups of strawberries.

   C. Janie can use approximately 5 cups of strawberries for each pie.

7. A sandwich costs $5.95 and a glass of milk costs $1.25. The cashier is calculating the bill.

   Which statement is correct?

   A. The cashier must add the exact amounts.

   B. The cashier can round the prices before adding.

© K12 Inc. All rights reserved.

TRY IT

8. Roberto wants to buy a T-shirt that costs $8.99, a pair of sandals that cost $4.79, and a baseball cap that costs $5.98. Roberto has $20.00 to spend.

Which **two** statements are true?

   A. If Roberto calculates exactly how much he will spend, he will know that the cashier is charging him the correct amount of money.

   B. If Roberto estimates the total cost by adding $9 + 5 + 6$, he will know that he has enough money to buy the three things.

   C. If Roberto rounds the amounts and adds $9 + 5 + 6$, he will be able to check to make sure the cashier gave him the correct change.

9. The American marathon runner ran 5,824 miles in one year. The Swedish marathon runner ran 4,954 miles in one year. About how many miles did the two runners run altogether? (Give the answer to the nearest hundred.)

   A. 10,700 miles   B. 10,800 miles   C. 10,900 miles   D. 11,000 miles

10. The observation deck on the Empire State Building is 1,211 feet from the ground. The observation deck on the Eiffel Tower is 902 feet from the ground. About how much higher is the deck on the Empire State Building than the Eiffel Tower? (Give the answer to the nearest ten.)

   A. 300 feet   B. 310 feet   C. 320 feet   D. 400 feet

11. Martin traveled 1,985 miles each business trip. He took 12 business trips in one year. About how far did Martin travel for business trips in one year? (Give the answer to the nearest thousand.)

   A. 2,000 miles   B. 12,000 miles   C. 20,000 miles   D. 24,000 miles

12. Frank needed to drive 2,420 miles. He wanted to drive the distance in 6 days, and he wanted to drive the same distance each day. About how far will he drive each day? (Give the answer to the nearest hundred.)

   A. 14,400 miles   B. 4,000 miles   C. 500 miles   D. 400 miles

13. The cafeteria bought 32 pounds of cheese for $116. About how much did 1 pound of cheese cost? (Give the answer to the nearest dollar.)

   A. $2   B. $3   C. $4   D. $5

© K12 Inc. All rights reserved.

TRY IT

Define and Sketch Triangles

Classify Triangles

Solve.

1. What is the name of a triangle that has only 2 of its 3 sides the same length?

2. How is an acute triangle different from both an obtuse triangle and a right triangle?

Name the triangle by its angles and its side lengths.

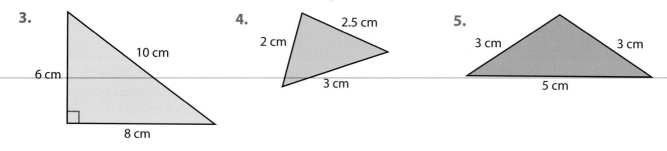

3.
6 cm
10 cm
8 cm

4.
2 cm
2.5 cm
3 cm

5.
3 cm
3 cm
5 cm

Draw.

6. Use a ruler and an index card to draw an obtuse scalene triangle.

7. Use a ruler to draw an equilateral triangle.

8. Use a ruler to draw an obtuse scalene triangle.

Choose the answer.

9. Which best describes an equilateral triangle?

   A. All sides are the same length; all angles have the same measure.

   B. Two sides are the same length; one angle measures 90°.

   C. Two sides are the same length; all angles measure less than 90°.

   D. Two sides are the same length; one angle measures greater than 90°.

10. Which best describes a right isosceles triangle?

   A. Two sides are the same length; one angle measures 90°.

   B. All sides are the same length; two angles measure 90°.

   C. All sides are different lengths; one angle measures 90°.

   D. Two sides are the same length; one angle measures greater than 90°.

© K12 Inc. All rights reserved.

T R Y   I T

11. Which triangle always has 1 right angle and 2 sides the same length?

A. acute isosceles

B. right isosceles

C. right equilateral

D. acute scalene

12. Which triangle always has all sides different lengths and all angles measuring less than 90°?

A. obtuse equilateral

B. acute scalene

C. equilateral

D. obtuse isosceles

13. Which seems to best describe this triangle?

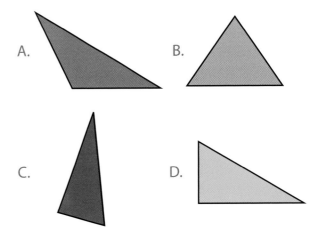

A. All sides are the same length; all angles are the same.

B. Two sides are the same length; one angle measures 90°.

C. Two sides are the same length; all angles are less than 90°.

D. Two sides are the same length; one angle is obtuse.

14. Which appears to be an equilateral triangle?

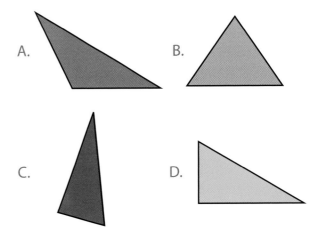

A.

B.

C.

D.

15. Which name correctly classifies this triangle?

3 in.   3 in.

2.5 in.

A. acute isosceles

B. obtuse equilateral

C. acute scalene

D. obtuse isosceles

16. Which name correctly classifies this triangle?

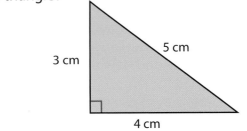

3 cm

5 cm

4 cm

A. right isosceles

B. obtuse equilateral

C. acute scalene

D. right scalene

© K12 Inc. All rights reserved.

TRY IT

Define and Sketch Quadrilaterals (A)

Identify Quadrilaterals

Answer the question.

1. How are these two shapes alike and how are they different?

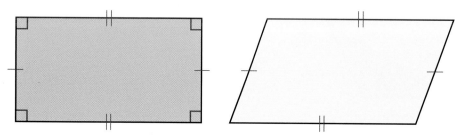

2. How are these two shapes alike and how are they different?

 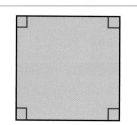

Read the problem and follow the directions.

3. Use a ruler to draw a parallelogram and a trapezoid. Explain how these two shapes are alike and how they are different.

4. Use a ruler to draw a rectangle and a square. Explain how these two shapes are alike and how they are different.

Choose the answer.

5. Which shape has one pair of opposite sides that are parallel but not equal in length?

    A. parallelogram

    B. square

    C. trapezoid

    D. rhombus

6. Which statement is true for all rectangles?

    A. All sides are equal in length.

    B. All angles are right angles.

    C. All angles are acute.

    D. Two angles are obtuse and two angles are acute.

© K12 Inc. All rights reserved.

7. Which best describes this quadrilateral?

   A. polygon with all right angles

   B. polygon with exactly one pair of sides that are equal in length

   C. polygon with exactly one pair of parallel sides

   D. polygon with four sides that are equal in length

8. Which shape has opposite sides that are both equal in length and parallel?

   A. triangle

   B. trapezoid

   C. pentagon

   D. parallelogram

9. Which shape has 4 congruent sides?

   A. circle

   B. trapezoid

   C. rhombus

   D. triangle

10. Choose **all** the names that could be used to classify this shape.

   A. quadrilateral

   B. trapezoid

   C. parallelogram

   D. rectangle

11. Choose **all** the names that could be used to classify this shape.

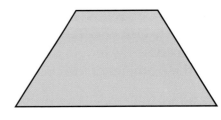

   A. rhombus

   B. parallelogram

   C. quadrilateral

   D. trapezoid

© K12 Inc. All rights reserved.

T R Y I T

Identify Diameters and Radii of Circles
Radius, Diameter, and Circumference

Worked Examples

If you know the length of the radius of a circle, you can find its diameter. If you know the length of a diameter of a circle, you can find its radius. If you know the diameter of a circle, you can also estimate its circumference.

PROBLEM Use the circle to answer the questions. If the length of the diameter, line segment PR or $\overline{PR}$ of the circle is 14 cm, what is its radius? What is the approximate circumference of the circle?

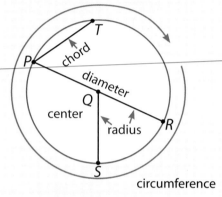

SOLUTION

UNDERSTAND THE PROBLEM Review the terms *radius, diameter,* and *circumference*. Use the length of the diameter to find its radius. Next use the length of the diameter of the circle to estimate its circumference.

DEVISE A PLAN Break this multistep problem into simpler parts.

1 Find the radius of the circle.

- A *radius* is a segment that has one endpoint at the center of the circle and the other endpoint on the circle. Examples are $\overline{QP}$, $\overline{QS}$, and $\overline{QR}$.

- A *diameter* is a segment that passes through the center of the circle and has both its endpoints on the circle. A diameter is formed by two radii (plural of radius).

- The diameter of a circle is two times the length of its radius. So the radius is one-half of the length of the diameter of the circle.

- To find the radius of this circle, write a number sentence to find half of 14 cm or 14 cm divided by 2. Then solve.

© K12 Inc. All rights reserved.

L E A R N

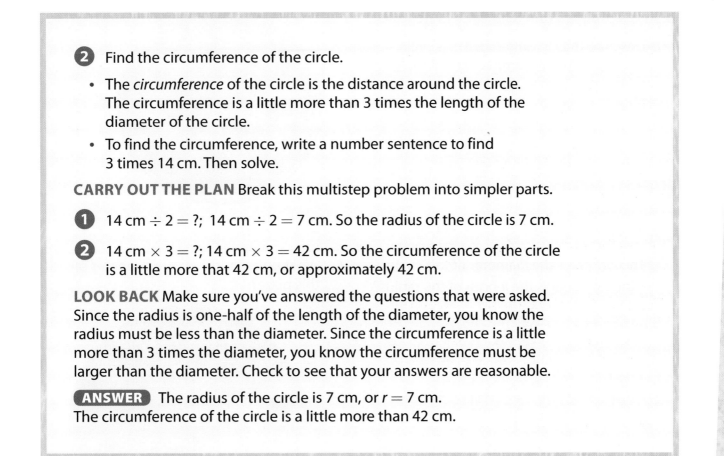

2 Find the circumference of the circle.

- The *circumference* of the circle is the distance around the circle. The circumference is a little more than 3 times the length of the diameter of the circle.

- To find the circumference, write a number sentence to find 3 times 14 cm. Then solve.

CARRY OUT THE PLAN Break this multistep problem into simpler parts.

1 14 cm ÷ 2 = ?; 14 cm ÷ 2 = 7 cm. So the radius of the circle is 7 cm.

2 14 cm × 3 = ?; 14 cm × 3 = 42 cm. So the circumference of the circle is a little more that 42 cm, or approximately 42 cm.

LOOK BACK Make sure you've answered the questions that were asked. Since the radius is one-half of the length of the diameter, you know the radius must be less than the diameter. Since the circumference is a little more than 3 times the diameter, you know the circumference must be larger than the diameter. Check to see that your answers are reasonable.

ANSWER The radius of the circle is 7 cm, or $r = 7$ cm. The circumference of the circle is a little more than 42 cm.

Answer the question.

1. What part of the circle is segment *AC*?

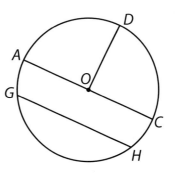

© K12 Inc. All rights reserved.

L E A R N

Read the problem and follow the directions.

2. Describe the circumference of a circle. Then trace the circumferences of three different circles on the dartboard with your finger.

Solve.

3. The length of the diameter of this circle is 3 inches. What is the length of the radius?

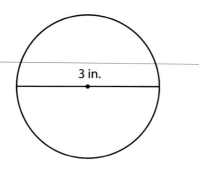

3 in.

4. What is the length of the diameter of this pizza?

15 cm

5. The diameter of this circle is 5 inches. About how many inches is the circle's circumference?

6. The diameter of the dart board is 18 inches. About how many inches is the circumference of the dart board?

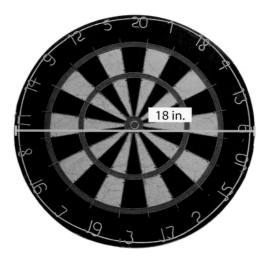

18 in.

© K12 Inc. All rights reserved.

Congruent Figures

Find Exact Matches

© K12 Inc. All rights reserved.

Worked Examples

Congruent figures are plane figures that have the same shape and size, regardless of their position. If you can slide, turn, or flip figures so that they fit exactly over one another, then the figures are congruent.

PROBLEM Which two figures are congruent? Explain your answer.

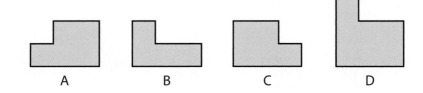

A   B   C   D

SOLUTION

UNDERSTAND THE PROBLEM Find out which two figures have exactly the same shape and size.

DEVISE A PLAN

1 Find two figures that look as if they are exactly the same shape and size. Then trace and cut out one of those two figures.

2 Next slide, turn, or flip the cutout figure so that it fits exactly over one of the other figures.

CARRY OUT THE PLAN

1 Identify the two figures that look congruent. Then trace and cut out one of them. Since Figure A and Figure C look congruent, you can trace and cut out Figure A.

2 Next flip Figure A so that it fits over Figure C with all edges matching exactly.

LOOK BACK Make sure you've answered the question that was asked. Since Figures A and C fit exactly over each other, they have the same shape and size. So Figures A and C are congruent and the answer makes sense.

ANSWER Figure A and Figure C are congruent figures. First I found for two figures that appeared congruent, Figures A and C. Then I traced and cut out Figure A. I flipped Figure A and placed it on top of Figure C. The two figures fit exactly with all edges matching. So I knew they were the same shape and size, or congruent figures.

Choose the two congruent figures.

1.

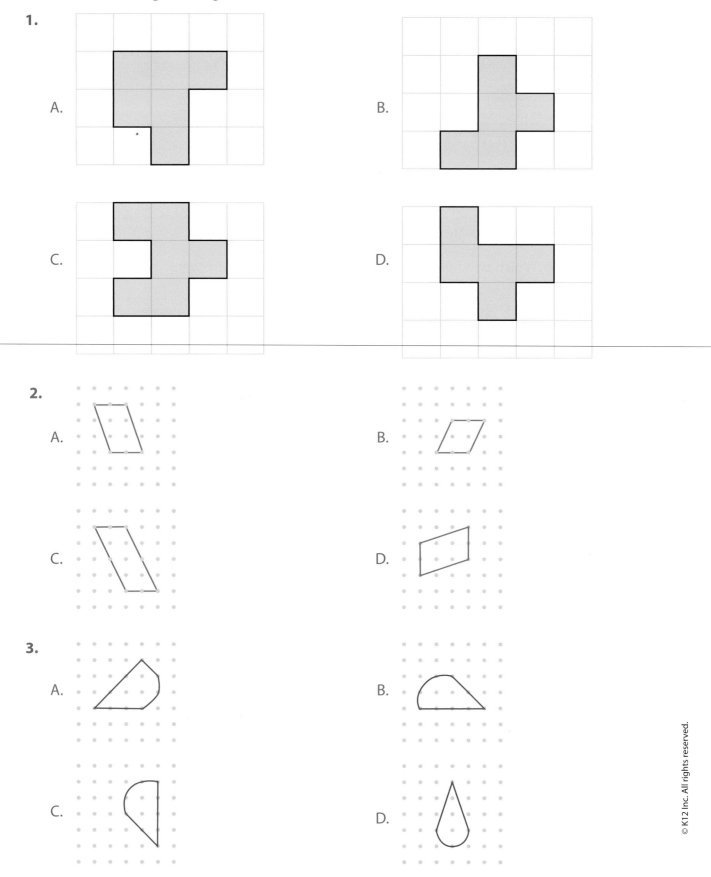

A.

B.

C.

D.

2.

A.

B.

C.

D.

3.

A.

B.

C.

D.

© K12 Inc. All rights reserved.

4.

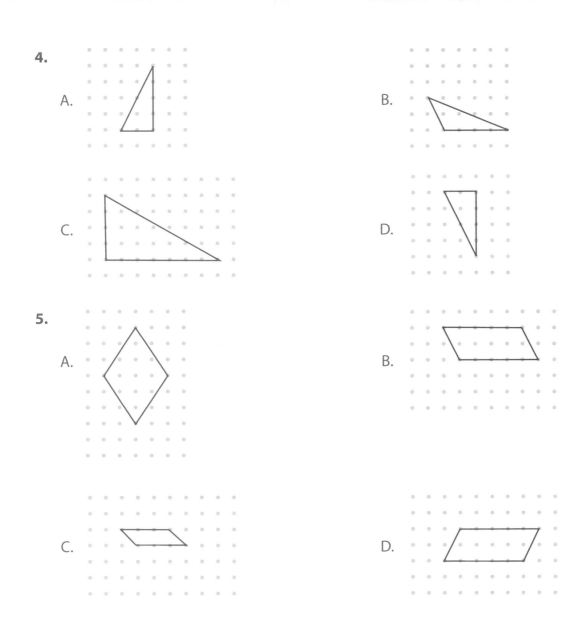

A.

B.

C.

D.

5.

A.

B.

C.

D.

© K12 Inc. All rights reserved.

LEARN

Congruent Figures

Explain Congruent and Similar Figures

Read the problem and follow the directions.

1. Are these two figures congruent? Explain your answer.

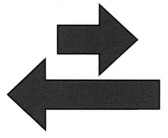

2. Explain what makes the following figures similar, but not congruent.

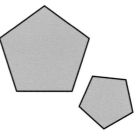

3. Are these two triangles congruent? Explain your answer.

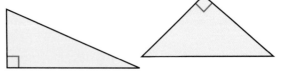

4. Are these two trapezoids congruent? Explain your answer.

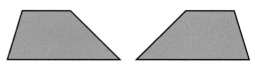

Choose the answer.

5. Look at the two quadrilaterals. Which statement is true?

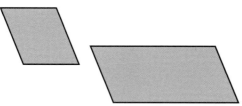

   A. The quadrilaterals are congruent because they are both parallelograms.

   B. The quadrilaterals are not congruent because they have different shapes.

   C. The quadrilaterals are congruent because if you turn one, they will match exactly.

   D. The quadrilaterals are similar but not congruent.

6. Look at the two triangles. Which statement is true?

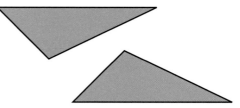

   A. The two figures are not congruent because they are different shapes.

   B. The two figures are not congruent because they are the same shape but not the same size.

   C. The two figures are congruent because they are the same size and shape.

   D. The two figures are similar, but not congruent.

© K12 Inc. All rights reserved.

7. Which shape is congruent to this blue shape?

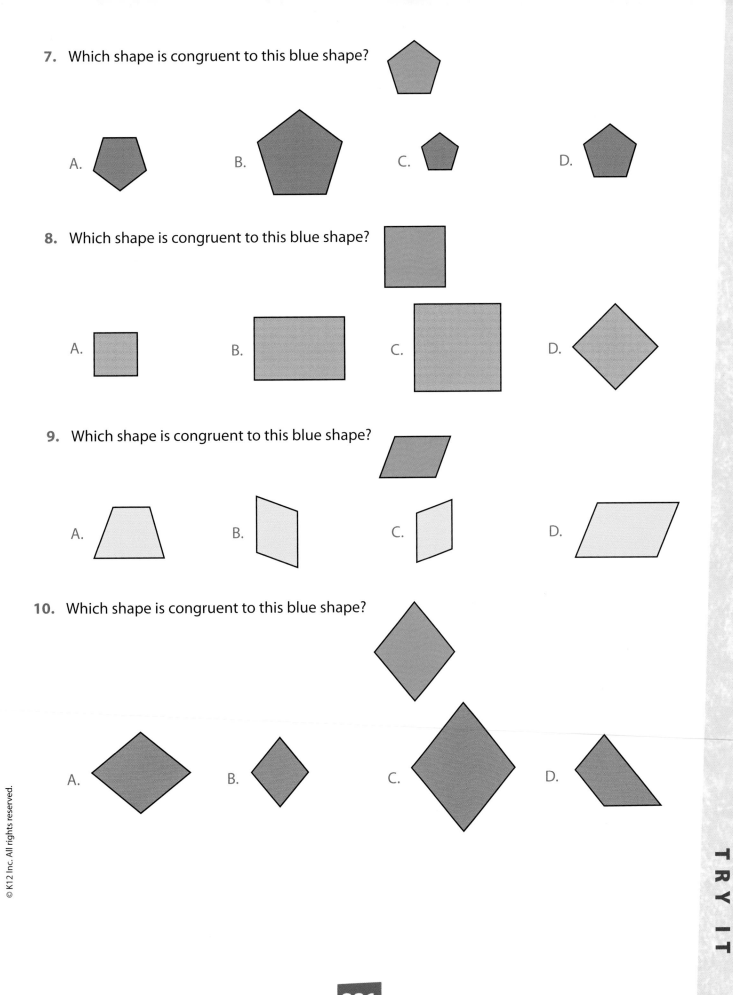

A.

B.

C.

D.

8. Which shape is congruent to this blue shape?

A.

B.

C.

D.

9. Which shape is congruent to this blue shape?

A.

B.

C.

D.

10. Which shape is congruent to this blue shape?

A.

B.

C.

D.

© K12 Inc. All rights reserved.

TRY IT

11. Look at the two parallelograms. Which statement is true?

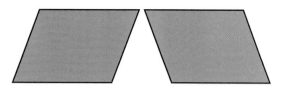

  A. The two parallelograms are congruent because one parallelogram was flipped, and it exactly matches the other one.

  B. The two parallelograms are not congruent.

  C. The two parallelograms are congruent because one parallelogram was slid, and it exactly matches the other one.

12. Look at the two rectangles. Which statement is true?

  A. The two rectangles are congruent because one rectangle was slid, and it exactly matches the other one.

  B. The two rectangles are not congruent.

  C. The two rectangles are congruent because one rectangle was flipped, and it exactly matches the other one.

13. Look at the two rectangles. Which statement is true?

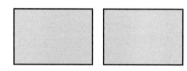

  A. The two shapes are congruent because they are the same size and the same shape.

  B. The two shapes are not congruent because they are the same size but not the same shape.

  C. The two shapes are not congruent because they are the same shape but not the same size.

14. Look at the two shapes. Which statement is true?

  A. The two shapes are not congruent because they are the same size but not the same shape.

  B. The two shapes are not congruent because they are the same shape but not the same size.

  C. The two shapes are congruent because they are the same size and the same shape.

© K12 Inc. All rights reserved.

TRY IT

Two Kinds of Symmetry

Different Kinds of Symmetry

© K12 Inc. All rights reserved.

Worked Examples

There are two kinds of symmetry. When a plane figure is folded along one or more lines so that the outside boundaries fit exactly on top of each other, the figure has *line symmetry*. When a plane figure is rotated 360° around its center point so that its outside boundaries realign at least once between the start and end of the turn, the figure has *rotational symmetry*.

PROBLEM 1 Does the figure below have line symmetry? If yes, sketch its line or lines of symmetry. If no, explain why there is no line of symmetry.

SOLUTION

UNDERSTAND THE PROBLEM Decide if the figure can be folded along one or more lines so that its outside boundaries match exactly. Draw the line or lines of symmetry, or explain why you cannot draw a line of symmetry.

DEVISE A PLAN Trace the figure on a sheet of paper. Then fold and refold the shape until the outside boundaries fit exactly on top of each other. Then draw the figure and the line of symmetry or lines of symmetry that you found, or explain why the figure has no line of symmetry.

CARRY OUT THE PLAN

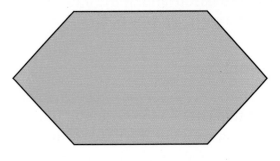

LEARN

LOOK BACK Since you can draw at least one line of symmetry, the figure has line symmetry. Make sure you've answered the yes-or-no question. Then draw the figure and the lines of symmetry. You do not need to write an explanation.

ANSWER Yes, the figure has line symmetry.

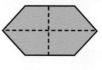

PROBLEM 2 Does the figure have rotational symmetry? If yes, state the degree of the rotation and the fraction of the turn at each location. If no, explain why not.

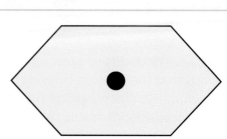

SOLUTION

UNDERSTAND THE PROBLEM Decide if the figure can be rotated 360° around its center point so that its outside boundaries align exactly. For each place this happens, name the rotation by the degree measure and by the fraction of a turn. If the figure does not have rotational symmetry, explain why not.

DEVISE A PLAN

- Trace the figure on a sheet of paper.

- Then push your pencil tip through the center and begin rotating the figure through a quarter turn (90°), a half turn (180°), a three-quarter turn (270°), and end at a full turn (360°).

- Before the shape has made one full turn, look for a place where the figure looks the same as it did before the rotation began.

- Name each point at which the figure has rotational symmetry, or explain why the figure does not have rotational symmetry.

CARRY OUT THE PLAN

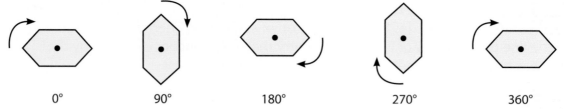

0° 90° 180° 270° 360°

LOOK BACK When you rotate the figure 180°, the outside boundaries of the figure realign so it looks the same as it did at the start of the turn. Make sure you've answered the yes-or-no question. Since the figure has rotational symmetry, you do not need to write an explanation.

ANSWER Yes, the figure has rotational symmetry. After a 180° rotation, or half turn, it looks the same as it did at the start.

© K12 Inc. All rights reserved.

Write Yes if the figure has line symmetry and No if it doesn't.
If yes, trace the shape and draw the line or lines of symmetry.

1.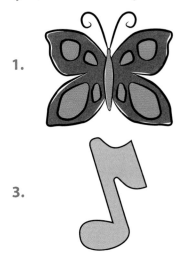

2.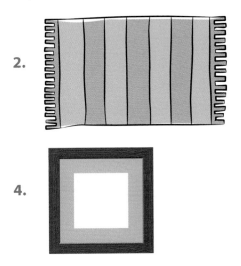

3.

4.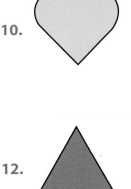

Draw the figure.

5. Draw a triangle that has no lines of symmetry.

6. Draw a triangle that has 1 line of symmetry.

7. Draw a triangle that has 3 lines of symmetry.

8. Draw a shape that has both line symmetry and rotational symmetry.

Write Yes if the figure has line symmetry and No if it doesn't.

9.

10.

11.

12.

© K12 Inc. All rights reserved.

L E A R N

Two Kinds of Symmetry

Find Symmetry

Choose the answer.

1. Which figure has line symmetry?

   A. 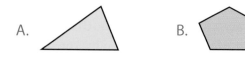   B.   C.   D.

2. Which figure has rotational symmetry?

   A.   B.   C.    D.

3. Which figure has rotational symmetry?

   A.    B.   C.   D.

4. Which picture has rotational symmetry?

   A. 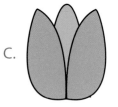   B.

   C.   D.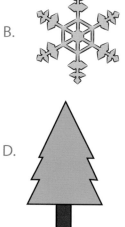

© K12 Inc. All rights reserved.

TRY IT

5. How many lines of symmetry does this rectangle have?

A. 0

B. 2

C. 3

D. 4

6. How many lines of symmetry does this square have?

A. 6

B. 5

C. 4

D. 3

7. How many lines of symmetry does this butterfly have?

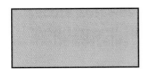

A. 1

B. 2

C. 4

D. 6

8. How many lines of symmetry does this letter have?

A. 0

B. 1

C. 2

D. 4

© K12 Inc. All rights reserved.

TRY IT

Describe Geometric Solids

Faces, Vertices, and Edges

Worked Examples

The number of faces, edges, and vertices are often used to identify and describe geometric solids. The number of faces, edges, and vertices of a solid are also related in other ways.

PROBLEM Count the number of faces, vertices, and edges of the solid shown. Record your answers on the data table.

Solid	Number of Faces	Number of Vertices	Number of Edges
cube	?	?	?

SOLUTION

1 Number of faces: Count, one by one, all the flat surfaces, or faces, of the cube. There are 6 faces.

2 Number of vertices: Count, one by one, the number of points where 3 or more edges of the cube meet. There are 8 vertices.

3 Number of edges: Count, one by one, where 2 faces of the cube meet. There are 12 edges.

Also, if you know two of your values, you can find the third value by using the equation $F + V - 2 = E$, where F is the number of faces, V is the number of vertices, and E is the number of edges.

ANSWER 6 faces, 8 vertices, 12 edges

© K12 Inc. All rights reserved.

Complete the chart. Count the bases of a prism and the base of a pyramid as *faces* of the geometric solids.

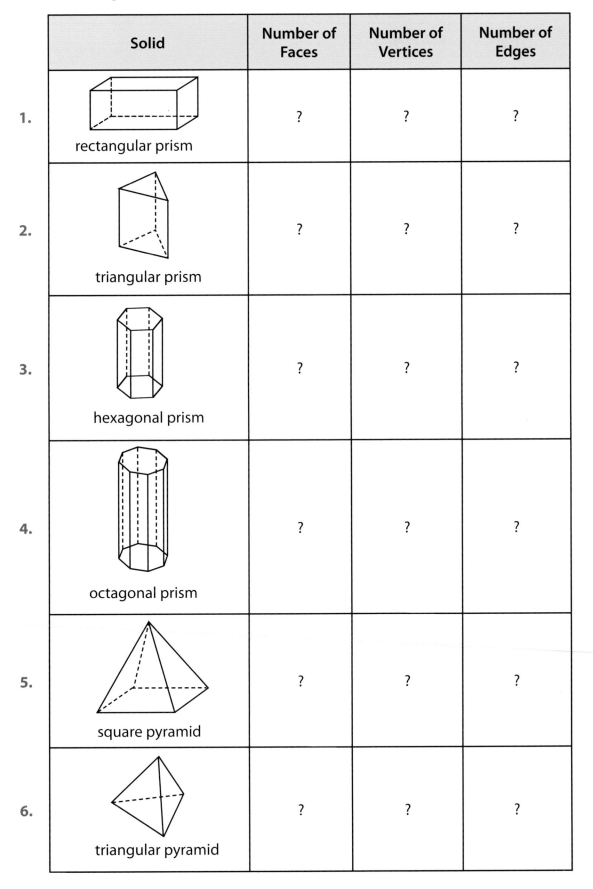

	Solid	Number of Faces	Number of Vertices	Number of Edges
1.	rectangular prism	?	?	?
2.	triangular prism	?	?	?
3.	hexagonal prism	?	?	?
4.	octagonal prism	?	?	?
5.	square pyramid	?	?	?
6.	triangular pyramid	?	?	?

© K12 Inc. All rights reserved.

L E A R N

Describe Geometric Solids

Cylinders, Cones, and Spheres

Worked Examples

The number of faces, edges, and vertices are often used to identify and describe many geometric solids. A *face* is a flat surface of a solid figure. An *edge* is the boundary where two faces meet or where a face and a curved surface meet. A *vertex* (plural: vertices) is the point at which 3 or more edges meet. The point of a cone is also a *vertex*.

PROBLEM 1 How many faces does a cone have? How many vertices? How many edges?

SOLUTION

1. Number of faces: The cone has 1 flat surface, so it has 1 face.

2. Number of vertices: The figure is a cone. The point of a cone is its vertex, so it has 1 vertex.

3. Number of edges: The face of the cone is a circle that meets a curved surface. Where the face and the curved surface meet is the edge of the cone. The cone has 1 edge.

ANSWER A cone has 1 face, 1 vertex, and 1 edge.

Complete the chart.

	Solid	Number of Faces	Number of Vertices	Number of Edges
1.	cylinder	?	?	?
2.	cone	?	?	?
3.	sphere	?	?	?

© K12 Inc. All rights reserved.

Geometric Nets

Sketch Nets

Worked Examples

A net is made by "opening" a solid figure and laying flat its faces. When a net is refolded, it should make the original three-dimensional figure.

PROBLEM Sketch the net of the square pyramid below. You may use the incomplete net on the right to help you.

SOLUTION

1. Describe all the faces of the square pyramid, even those you cannot see. There are 4 triangles and 1 square base. Each triangle is touching 1 side of the pyramid's square base.

2. Visualize what the net would look like if it were opened at the vertex where the triangles meet and then unfolded to lie flat. Sketch the net.

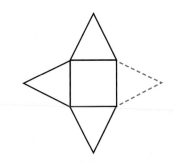

ANSWER

© K12 Inc. All rights reserved.

L E A R N

Look at the solid figure and its partial net. Sketch the completed net.

1. triangular prism

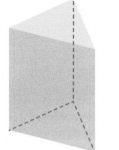 

2. cylinder

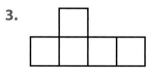

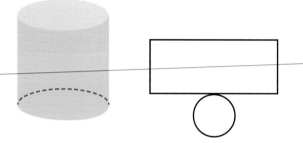

Complete the net so it could be folded to form a solid figure.
Name the figure.

3.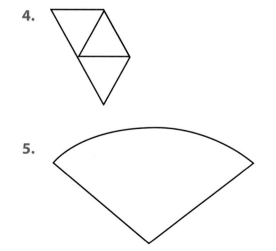

4.

5.

© K12 Inc. All rights reserved.

Geometric Nets

Identify Nets

Write the name of the 3-D figure that the net represents.

1.

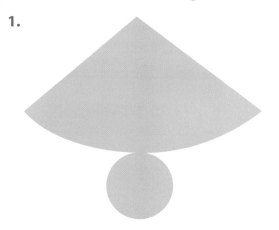

2.

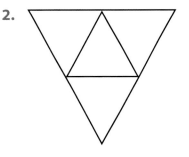

Read the problem and follow the directions.

3. Complete this net so it can be folded to form a cube.

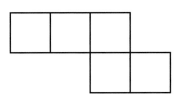

4. Complete this net so it can be folded to form a triangular prism.

© K12 Inc. All rights reserved.

T R Y   I T

5. Sketch a net of a cube, making a different net from the net in Problem 3.

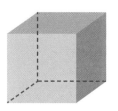

6. Sketch a net of a square pyramid.

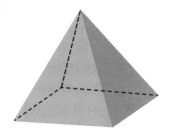

Choose the net of the 3-D figure.

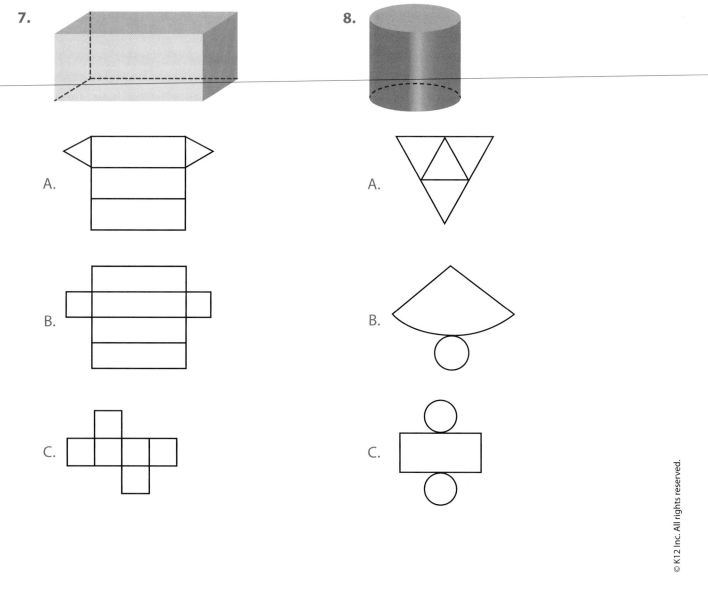

7.

A.

B.

C.

8.

A.

B.

C.

© K12 Inc. All rights reserved.

TRY IT

Count with Negative Numbers (A)

Count Backward and Forward

Worked Examples

You can identify a pattern to find the missing numbers in a number sequence. First figure out how much the given numbers increase or decrease. Then apply this pattern to complete the sequence.

PROBLEM What numbers are missing in this number sequence?

$^-12, ^-10, ^-8, \underline{\ ?\ }, \underline{\ ?\ }, ^-2, 0, ^+2$

⟵ ┼┼┼┼┼┼┼┼┼┼┼┼┼┼┼┼┼┼┼┼┼┼┼┼┼┼┼ ⟶
$^-12\ ^-11\ ^-10\ ^-9\ ^-8\ ^-7\ ^-6\ \ ^-5\ ^-4\ ^-3\ \ ^-2\ ^-1\ \ 0\ \ ^+1\ ^+2\ ^+3\ \ ^+4\ ^+5\ \ ^+6\ ^+7\ \ ^+8\ \ ^+9\ ^+10\ ^+11\ ^+12\ ^+13\ ^+14$

SOLUTION

1 Decide whether the number sequence is counting forward or backward. This sequence is counting forward.

2 Determine what the pattern is. This pattern is "count forward by 2s."

3 Find the starting number on a number line. Count forward, following the pattern. Use your finger to help keep track of the jumps. When you get to the first missing number, look at where your finger is on the number line. Write the missing number.

4 Continue counting till you reach the end of the number sequence. Use the number line to find any missing numbers.

5 To check your answer, show the complete pattern on the number line.

ANSWER The missing numbers are $^-6$ and $^-4$.

© K12 Inc. All rights reserved.

Answer the question.

1. What is the next number in this pattern?

$^+6, ^+3, 0, ^-3, ^-6, \underline{\ ?\ }$

$^-10\ \ ^-9\ \ ^-8\ \ ^-7\ \ ^-6\ \ ^-5\ \ ^-4\ \ ^-3\ \ ^-2\ \ ^-1\ \ 0\ \ ^+1\ \ ^+2\ \ ^+3\ \ ^+4\ \ ^+5\ \ ^+6\ \ ^+7\ \ ^+8\ \ ^+9\ \ ^+10$

L E A R N

2. The numbers in this pattern increase by the same amount each time. What are the next three numbers in the pattern?

   $^-11, ^-9, ^-7, ^-5, ^-3,$ __?__ , __?__ , __?__

3. Serena is counting backward by 8s. If she starts counting at 16, what two numbers are missing?

   $^+16, ^+8, 0, ^-8,$ __?__ , __?__ , $^-32$

Read the problem and follow the directions.

4. Count backward by 5s from $^+20$ to $^-25$ and write your number sequence.

5. Count forward by 4s from $^-20$ to $^+4$ and write your number sequence.

© K12 Inc. All rights reserved.

LEARN

Count with Negative Numbers (A)

Find Missing Numbers

Read the problem and follow the directions.

1. Count backward by 3s from $^+6$ to $^-15$ and write the number sequence.

2. Count forward by 2s from $^-13$ to $^-1$ and write the number sequence.

3. Count backward by 2s from $^+7$ to $^-11$ and write your number sequence.

4. Count forward by 5s from $^-25$ to $^+15$ and write your number sequence.

Answer the question.

5. The numbers in this pattern decrease by the same amount each time. What are the next three numbers in the pattern?

   $^+10, 0, ^-10, ^-20, ^-30, \underline{\ ?\ }, \underline{\ ?\ }, \underline{\ ?\ }$

6. Rosa is counting by 6s. If she starts counting at $^-18$, what two numbers are missing?

   $^-18, ^-12, \underline{\ ?\ }, \underline{\ ?\ }, ^+6, ^+12, ^+18$

Choose the answer.

7. What is the next integer in this pattern?

   $^+15, ^+10, ^+5, 0, ^-5, ^-10, \underline{\ ?\ }$

   A. $^-5$ B. $^-20$

   C. $^-15$ D. $^+5$

8. What is the next integer in this pattern?

   $^+6, ^+4, ^+2, 0, ^-2, ^-4, ^-6, \underline{\ ?\ }$

   A. $^-2$ B. $^-8$

   C. $^+2$ D. $^-4$

9. Which integer is missing in this pattern?

   $^+7, ^+3, ^-1, \underline{\ ?\ }, ^-9, ^-13$

   A. $^-5$ B. $^-3$

   C. $^+4$ D. $^-4$

10. What is the next integer in this pattern?

    $^+11, ^+7, ^+3, ^-1, ^-5, ^-9, \underline{\ ?\ }$

    A. $^-13$ B. $^-4$

    C. $^-10$ D. $^+4$

11. Which integer is missing in this pattern?

    $11, 6, 1, ^-4, \underline{\ ?\ }, ^-14, ^-19$

    A. $^-5$ B. $^-9$

    C. $^-11$ D. $^+5$

© K12 Inc. All rights reserved.

TRY IT

Count with Negative Numbers (B)

Predict Number Patterns

You can predict a missing number in a counting pattern that has negative numbers.

PROBLEM The numbers in this pattern decrease by the same amount each time. What is the 10th number in the pattern?

$^-16, ^-18, ^-20, ^-22, ^-24, \underline{\ ?\ }, \underline{\ ?\ }, \underline{\ ?\ }, \underline{\ ?\ }, \underline{\ ?\ }$

SOLUTION

1 Write the sequence.

2 Decide whether the number sequence is counting forward or backward. This sequence is counting backward.

3 Determine what the pattern is. This pattern is "count backward by 2s."

4 Count backward from the starting number, following the pattern. For this problem, start with $^-16$, count back by 2, and the next number is $^-18$.

5 Continue counting backward. When you get to the first missing number, write that number ($^-26$).

6 Repeat Step 5 to find the remaining missing numbers: $^-28, ^-30, ^-32, ^-34$.

7 Look at the 10th number to get your answer.

8 To check your answer, make sure all the numbers in the sequence follow the pattern.

ANSWER The 10th number is $^-34$.

Find the missing numbers.

1. The numbers in this pattern decrease by the same amount each time. What are the next three numbers in the pattern?

   $^-8, ^-12, ^-16, ^-20, ^-24, \underline{\ ?\ }, \underline{\ ?\ }, \underline{\ ?\ }$

© K12 Inc. All rights reserved.

LEARN

2. Steve is counting backward by 6s. If he starts counting at $^+6$, what are the next three numbers in this pattern?

$^+6, 0, ^-6, ^-12, ^-18, \underline{\ ?\ }, \underline{\ ?\ }, \underline{\ ?\ }$

3. Amy is counting backward by 7s. If she starts counting at $^+49$, what is the 12th number in the pattern?

$^+49, ^+42, ^+35, ^+28, ^+21, ^+14, \underline{\ ?\ }, \underline{\ ?\ }, \underline{\ ?\ }, \underline{\ ?\ }, \underline{\ ?\ }, \underline{\ ?\ }$

4. What is the 8th number in this pattern?

$^-18, ^-16, ^-14, ^-12, \underline{\ ?\ }, \underline{\ ?\ }, \underline{\ ?\ }, \underline{\ ?\ }$

5. What is the 10th number in this pattern?

$^-11, ^-9, ^-7, ^-5, ^-3, ^-1, ^+1, \underline{\ ?\ }, \underline{\ ?\ }, \underline{\ ?\ }$

6. What are the missing numbers in the pattern?

$^-20, ^-15, ^-10, \underline{\ ?\ }, \underline{\ ?\ }, \underline{\ ?\ }, ^+10, ^+15$

7. What is the missing number in the pattern?

$^-7, ^-4, \underline{\ ?\ }, ^+2, ^+5, ^+8, ^+11$

8. What is the missing number in this pattern?

$^-30, ^-27, ^-24, ^-21, ^-18, \underline{\ ?\ }$

Write a pattern problem.

9. Write a number-pattern problem that starts with a positive number and decreases so that the 10th number is negative.

© K12 Inc. All rights reserved.

LEARN

Count with Negative Numbers (B)

Solve Problems with Number Patterns

Find the missing numbers.

1. The numbers in this pattern increase by the same amount each time. What are the next three numbers in the pattern? ⁻27, ⁻24, ⁻21, ⁻18, _?_, _?_, _?_

2. Derek is counting backward by 4s. If he starts counting at ⁺20, what two numbers are missing? ⁺20, ⁺16, ⁺12, ⁺8, _?_, 0, ⁻4, _?_, ⁻12, ⁻16

Predict the number.

3. Rebecca is counting backward by 10s. If she starts counting at ⁺40, what is the 10th number in the pattern?
⁺40, ⁺30, ⁺20, ⁺10, 0, ⁻10, _?_, _?_, _?_, _?_

4. What is the 12th number in this pattern?
⁻45, ⁻50, ⁻55, ⁻60, ⁻65, _?_, _?_, _?_, _?_, _?_, _?_, _?_

5. What is the 15th number in this pattern?
⁻20, ⁻18, ⁻16, ⁻14, ⁻12, ⁻10, ⁻8, ⁻6, _?_, _?_, _?_, _?_, _?_, _?_, _?_

Choose the answer.

6. What is the 10th number in this pattern?

   ⁺14, ⁺7, 0, ⁻7, ⁻14, _?_, _?_, _?_, _?_, _?_

   A. ⁻7   B. ⁻28
   C. ⁻42   D. ⁻49

7. What is the 12th number in this pattern?

   ⁺12, ⁺10, ⁺8, ⁺6, ⁺4, _?_, _?_, _?_, _?_, _?_, _?_, _?_

   A. ⁻14   B. ⁻12
   C. ⁻8   D. ⁻10

8. What is the 8th number in this pattern?

   ⁺12, ⁺8, ⁺4, 0, _?_, _?_, _?_, _?_

   A. ⁻12   B. ⁻16
   C. ⁻8   D. ⁻4

9. What is the 7th number in this pattern?

   36, 24, 12, _?_, _?_, _?_, _?_

   A. ⁻12   C. ⁻36
   B. ⁻24   D. ⁻48

10. What is the 9th number in this pattern?

    ⁺11, ⁺6, ⁺1, ⁻4, ⁻9, ⁻14, _?_, _?_, _?_

    A. ⁻15   B. ⁻29
    C. ⁻19   D. ⁻5

11. What is the 10th number in this pattern?

    ⁺15, ⁺10, ⁺5, 0, _?_, _?_, _?_, _?_, _?_, _?_

    A. ⁻30   B. ⁻20
    C. ⁻5   D. ⁻10

© K12 Inc. All rights reserved.

TRY IT

Rational Numbers on a Number Line (B)

Compare Number Location

Worked Examples

You can mark the locations of positive and negative numbers on the same number line and compare their values.

PROBLEM Is $^-2$ located to the left or right of $^-1\frac{1}{4}$? Is $^-2$ greater than $^-1\frac{1}{4}$ or less than $^-1\frac{1}{4}$? Is $^-2$ greater than $^-1.25$ or less than $^-1.25$?

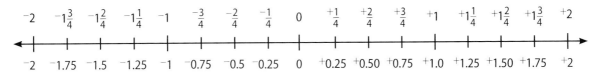

$^-2$ $^-1\frac{3}{4}$ $^-1\frac{2}{4}$ $^-1\frac{1}{4}$ $^-1$ $^-\frac{3}{4}$ $^-\frac{2}{4}$ $^-\frac{1}{4}$ 0 $^+\frac{1}{4}$ $^+\frac{2}{4}$ $^+\frac{3}{4}$ $^+1$ $^+1\frac{1}{4}$ $^+1\frac{2}{4}$ $^+1\frac{3}{4}$ $^+2$

$^-2$ $^-1.75$ $^-1.5$ $^-1.25$ $^-1$ $^-0.75$ $^-0.5$ $^-0.25$ 0 $^+0.25$ $^+0.50$ $^+0.75$ $^+1.0$ $^+1.25$ $^+1.50$ $^+1.75$ $^+2$

SOLUTION

1 Copy the number line.

2 Use one color marker to plot the point for $^-2$. Use another color marker to plot the point $^-1\frac{1}{4}$.

3 Look at the two points plotted. The point for $^-2$ is to the left of the point for $^-1\frac{1}{4}$. $^-1\frac{1}{4}$ is equivalent to $^-1.25$.

4 Since a number line shows numbers in order, numbers to the left are less than numbers to the right. So $^-2$ is less than $^-1\frac{1}{4}$ and $^-1.25$.

ANSWER Since $^-2$ is located to the left of $^-1\frac{1}{4}$, $^-2$ is less than $^-1\frac{1}{4}$ and its equivalent $^-1.25$.

Use the number line to answer Problems 1 and 2.

$^-2$ $^-1\frac{3}{4}$ $^-1\frac{2}{4}$ $^-1\frac{1}{4}$ $^-1$ $^-\frac{3}{4}$ $^-\frac{2}{4}$ $^-\frac{1}{4}$ 0 $^+\frac{1}{4}$ $^+\frac{2}{4}$ $^+\frac{3}{4}$ $^+1$ $^+1\frac{1}{4}$ $^+1\frac{2}{4}$ $^+1\frac{3}{4}$ $^+2$

$^-2$ $^-1.75$ $^-1.5$ $^-1.25$ $^-1$ $^-0.75$ $^-0.5$ $^-0.25$ 0 $^+0.25$ $^+0.50$ $^+0.75$ $^+1.0$ $^+1.25$ $^+1.50$ $^+1.75$ $^+2$

1. Is $\frac{1}{4}$ located to the right of 0.5 or to the left of 0.5?

2. Is $\frac{1}{4}$ greater than 0.5 or is $\frac{1}{4}$ less than 0.5?

© K12 Inc. All rights reserved.

L E A R N

Use the number line to answer Problems 3 and 4.

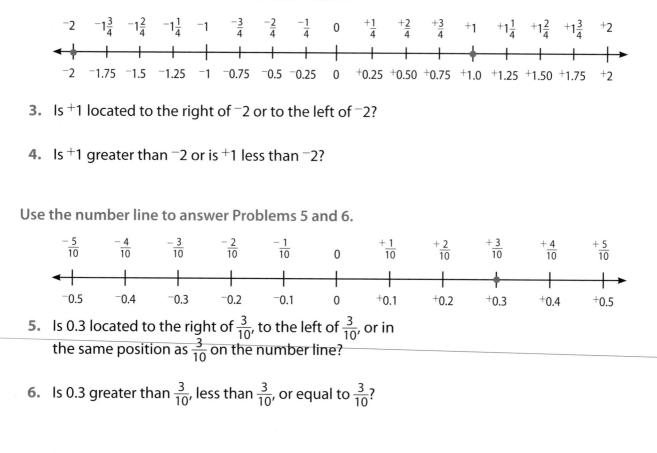

3. Is ⁺1 located to the right of ⁻2 or to the left of ⁻2?

4. Is ⁺1 greater than ⁻2 or is ⁺1 less than ⁻2?

Use the number line to answer Problems 5 and 6.

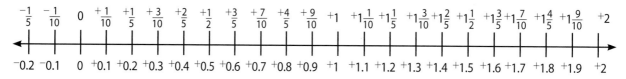

5. Is 0.3 located to the right of $\frac{3}{10}$, to the left of $\frac{3}{10}$, or in the same position as $\frac{3}{10}$ on the number line?

6. Is 0.3 greater than $\frac{3}{10}$, less than $\frac{3}{10}$, or equal to $\frac{3}{10}$?

Use the number line to answer Problems 7 and 8.

7. Is ⁻0.1 located to the right of ⁻0.2 or to the left of ⁻0.2?

8. Is ⁻0.1 greater than ⁻0.2 or less than ⁻0.2?

© K12 Inc. All rights reserved.

LEARN

Rational Numbers on a Number Line (C)

Work with Number Lines

Worked Examples

You can use what you know about integers, fractions, and decimal numbers to locate a point on a number line.

PROBLEM Which number line shows a point at $^+\frac{3}{5}$?

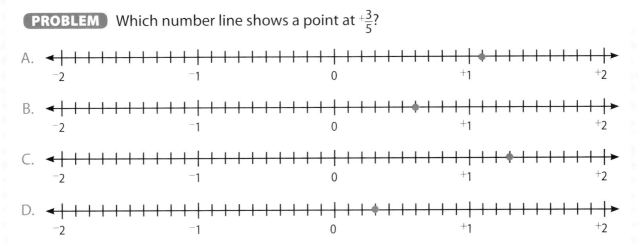

SOLUTION

UNDERSTAND THE PROBLEM Choose the number line that shows a point to the right of 0 that is $\frac{3}{5}$ the distance from 0 to $^+1$.

DEVISE A PLAN Use logical reasoning. Look at the number lines and rule out any number line that doesn't show a point at $^+\frac{3}{5}$. Look at the remaining number line. Make sure it shows the point at $^+\frac{3}{5}$.

CARRY OUT THE PLAN Think: $^+\frac{3}{5}$ is a fraction between 0 and $^+1$, so the points in A and C cannot be correct because they both show points to the right of $^+1$, or greater than $^+1$. The point in D is $\frac{3}{10}$ the distance from 0 to $^+1$, not $\frac{3}{5}$ the distance.

The point in B is $\frac{6}{10}$ the distance from 0 to $^+1$. Since $\frac{6 \div 2}{10 \div 2} = {}^+\frac{3}{5}$, the correct answer is B.

© K12 Inc. All rights reserved.

L E A R N

LOOK BACK Reread the question. Make sure the number line you chose shows the point at $\frac{+6}{10}$, or $\frac{+3}{5}$.

ANSWER   The number line in choice B shows a point at $\frac{+3}{5}$.

Read the problem and follow the directions.

1. Sketch a number line and graph $^-3$, $^+1$, and $^+2.5$ on the number line.

Answer the question.

2. The integer $^-2$ is located to the left of $^+1$ on the number line.
   Is $^-2$ greater than or less than $^+2$?

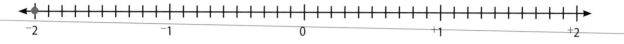

3. The integer $^-2$ is located to the right of $^-5$ on the number line.
   Is $^-2$ greater than or less than $^-5$?

Choose the answer.

4. Which number line shows a point at $^+0.25$?

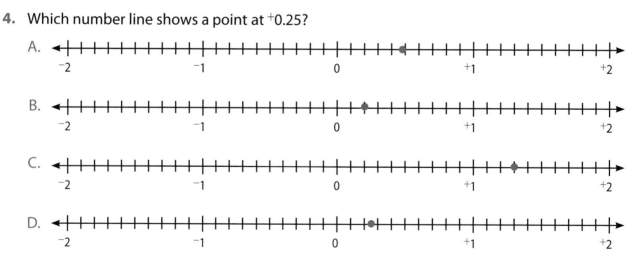

© K12 Inc. All rights reserved.

LEARN

5. Which number line shows $+1$, $+1.75$, and $+\frac{3}{10}$?

A.

B.

C.

D.

6. Point *S* represents $+1.5$ on this number line. Which statement is true about the location of $+1\frac{1}{5}$ on this number line?

A. $+1\frac{1}{5}$ is at the same point as point *S*.

B. $+1\frac{1}{5}$ is to the right of point *S*.

C. $+1\frac{1}{5}$ is to the left of point *S*.

D. You cannot determine the location of $+1\frac{1}{5}$ on the number line.

© K12 Inc. All rights reserved.

LEARN

Expressions and Equations

Algebraic Expressions and Equations

You can use variables to write algebraic expressions or equations that match different descriptions. You can use any symbol to stand for the unknown number. For example, you can use a triangle (▲) for the variable.

PROBLEM 1 Write an *expression* that matches this situation:

Katherine separates a pile of photos into five equal groups.

SOLUTION

UNDERSTAND THE PROBLEM
You are separating an unknown number of photos into 5 equal groups, or dividing an unknown number by 5.

DEVISE A PLAN Use (▲) to stand for the unknown number of photos.

CARRY OUT THE PLAN
$▲ \div 5$

LOOK BACK Make sure you've answered what was asked. Katherine separates photos into 5 equal groups, so the following expression makes sense: $▲ \div 5$.

ANSWER $▲ \div 5$

PROBLEM 2 Write an *equation* that matches this situation:

Leo had some batteries and then bought six more. He has thirteen batteries now.

SOLUTION

UNDERSTAND THE PROBLEM
"Bought six more" means addition, so you are adding 6 to an unknown number of batteries. "He has thirteen batteries now" means "equals 13."

DEVISE A PLAN Use (▲) to stand for the unknown number of batteries.

CARRY OUT THE PLAN
$▲ + 6 = 13$

LOOK BACK Make sure you've answered what was asked. Leo had some batteries and bought 6 more for a total of 13 batteries. So the following equation makes sense: $▲ + 6 = 13$.

ANSWER $▲ + 6 = 13$

© K12 Inc. All rights reserved.

LEARN

Read the situation. Use a triangle (▲) for the variable and explain what the variable represents. Then write the algebraic expression or equation that matches the situation.

1. Toby has three times as many trading cards as Ruth.
   Toby has twenty-four cards.

2. Joe bought a bag of chips.
   He ate twelve of them.
   He has eight chips left.

3. Amy has six stacks of CDs with the same number of CDs in each stack.

Read the situation. Use a question mark (?) for the variable and explain what the variable represents. Then write the algebraic expression or equation that matches the situation.

4. Jill walks five blocks to the library and then continues on to the grocery store.
   She walks a total of fifteen blocks.

5. Nathan has thirty party favors to divide among each of his friends.

Read the situation. Use a *p* for the variable and explain what the variable represents. Then write the algebraic expression or equation that matches the situation.

6. Lizzy scored twelve points in each basketball game this season.
   She scored a total of eighty-four points.

7. Adam had a bag of rocks.
   He lost eleven of them.
   He now has twenty-five rocks.

© K12 Inc. All rights reserved.

LEARN

Expressions and Equations

Expressions and Equations Practice

Read the problem or situation. Then write the expression or equation that matches the situation. To represent an unknown number, use a symbol or letter.

1. Write an expression that means twelve times an unknown number.

2. Lisa took twenty-five pictures on her digital camera. She deleted twelve of them. She then had thirteen pictures left on her camera. Write an equation that represents this situation.

3. Write an expression that represents the following:
    Jack had some peanuts in a bag. He ate nine of the peanuts.

4. Write an equation that represents the following:
    Janet has many pairs of shoes. She bought three more pairs. She now has sixteen pairs of shoes.

5. Write an expression that represents the following:
    There are 5 flowers in each of 6 vases.

Choose the answer.

6. Which expression means 9 more than a number?

    A. $n + 9$ B. $9 \times n$

    C. $n - 9$ D. $9 \div n$

7. Which expression means 10 less than a number?

    A. $a + 10$ B. $10 \times a$

    C. $a - 10$ D. $10 \div a$

8. Which expression means 12 divided by a number?

    A. $12 \div p$ B. $p + 12$

    C. $12 \times p$ D. $p - 12$

9. Candy divides some stamps into 4 equal groups. Which expression represents this situation?

    A. $\blacktriangle - 4$ B. $4 \times \blacktriangle$

    C. $\blacktriangle \div 4$ D. $4 + \blacktriangle$

10. Neil has 5 times as many pencils as Victor. Which expression represents this situation?

    A. $\blacktriangle - 5$ B. $5 \times \blacktriangle$

    C. $\blacktriangle \div 5$ D. $\blacktriangle + 5$

11. Which equation means that 12 decreased by a number is 4?

    A. $12 - 4 = n$ B. $12 - n = 4$

    C. $12 + 4 = n$ D. $4 \times 12 = n$

© K12 Inc. All rights reserved.

TRY IT

12. Which equation means a number divided by thirty is equal to 3?

    A. $30 + 3 = e$ B. $e \div 30 = 3$ C. $30 \times e = 3$ D. $30 - 3 = e$

13. Tim walked a number of steps around the park. Then he walked 10 more steps. He walked a total of 25 steps. Which equation represents this situation?

    A. $\square + 10 = 25$ B. $25 \times 10 = \square$ C. $25 + 10 = \square$ D. $10 - \square = 25$

14. Vanessa walked the same number of miles each day for 5 days. She walked a total of 20 miles. Which equation represents this situation?

    A. $20 + 5 = \square$ B. $20 - 5 = \square$ C. $\square \times 5 = 20$ D. $20 \times \square = 5$

15. Manny divided his collection of baseball cards equally among 4 of his friends. Each friend got 5 cards. Which equation represents this situation?

    A. $\square = 4 + 5$ B. $\square = 5 \div 4$ C. $\square \div 4 = 5$ D. $4 \times 5 = \square$

16. Kevin had some money. He spent $8. He has $20 left. Which equation represents this situation?

    A. $20 - \square = 8$ B. $20 - 8 = \square$ C. $\square + 8 = 20$ D. $\square - 8 = 20$

17. Which equation means ten increased by a number equals 22?

    A. $10 + t = 22$ B. $22 + 10 = t$ C. $t - 10 = 22$ D. $t \div 10 = 22$

18. Which equation means twenty divided by a number is equal to 10?

    A. $20 + d = 10$ B. $20 - d = 10$ C. $20 \div d = 10$ D. $20 \times d = 10$

19. James had some apples. He bought 5 more. Which expression represents this situation?

    A. $\blacktriangle - 5$ B. $5 \times \blacktriangle$ C. $\blacktriangle \div 5$ D. $\blacktriangle + 5$

20. Bonnie divides some cherries into 8 equal groups. Which expression represents this situation?

    A. $p - 8$ B. $p \div 8$ C. $p + 8$ D. $8 \times p$

© K12 Inc. All rights reserved.

Addition Property of Equality (A)

Complete the Equation

Write the number that should replace the question mark.

1. $5 = 5$
    $3 + 5 = 5 + \underline{\ ?\ }$

2. $9 = 9$
    $6 + 9 = 9 + \underline{\ ?\ }$

3. $8 = 4 + 4$
    $2 + 8 = 4 + 4 + \underline{\ ?\ }$

4. $1 + 6 = 7$
    $4 + 1 + 6 = 7 + \underline{\ ?\ }$

5. $10 = 2 + 8$
    $\underline{\ ?\ } + 10 = 2 + 8 + 9$

Choose the answer.

6. Marian and George have the same number of marbles. Each of them is given 4 more marbles. Which statement is true?

    A. Marian now has 4 more marbles than George.

    B. George now has 4 more marbles than Marian.

    C. Marian and George have the same number of marbles.

7. Darin and Tim have the same number of balloons. Each of them blows up 6 more balloons. Which statement is true?

    A. Darin and Tim have the same number of balloons.

    B. Darin now has 6 more balloons than Tim.

    C. Tim now has 6 more balloons than Darin.

8. Which number could replace the ▲?
    $4 = 4$
    $4 + 9 = ▲ + 4$

    A. 4

    B. 5

    C. 9

    D. 13

9. Which number could replace the ▲?
    $6 + 8 = 10 + 4$
    $6 + 8 + 5 = 10 + 4 + ▲$

    A. 5

    B. 14

    C. 19

    D. 28

© K12 Inc. All rights reserved.

TRY IT

Choose the answer. Circle the correct number of objects added
to each side.

10. Mark and Carrie found sea stars on the sand. Mark
put his sea stars into a pail. Carrie put her sea stars
on the table. They each collected the same number
of sea stars. Both Mark and Carrie found 3 more
sea stars.

Which picture is correct?

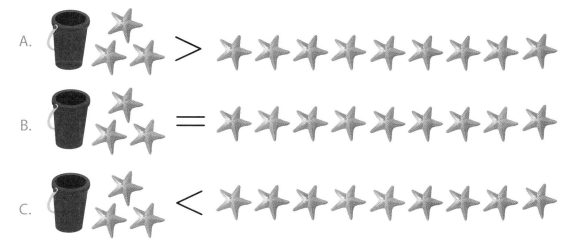

A.

B.

C.

11. Dave and Cara had some marbles. Dave put
his marbles into a jar. Cara put her marbles on
a chair. They each had the same number of
marbles. Dave and Cara were each given
4 more marbles.

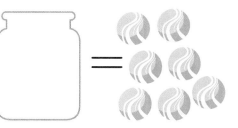

Which picture is correct?

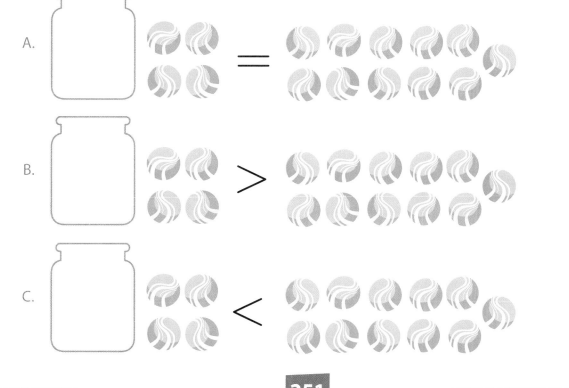

A.

B.

C.

© K12 Inc. All rights reserved.

12. Paula and Martine had some toy cars. Paula put her cars into a box. Martine put her cars on the table. They each had the same number of cars. Both Paula and Martine bought 7 more toy cars.

Which picture is correct?

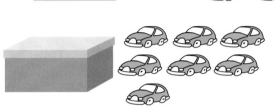

A.

B.

C.

13. Lara and Tom were given some seeds. Tom planted his seeds in a flowerbed. Lara left her seeds in a bowl overnight. They each were given the same number of seeds. Both Lara and Tom were given 3 more seeds.

Which picture is correct?

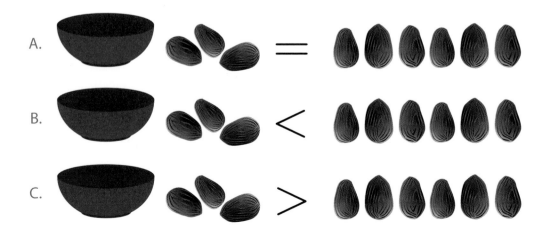

A.

B.

C.

© K12 Inc. All rights reserved.

TRY IT

Multiply by Equal Quantities (A)

Create Equal Quantities

Solve.

1. Draw a picture to show how to multiply the equation by 2.

$$7 = 3 + 4$$

2. Use your picture from Problem 1 complete each number sentence.

$$7 = 3 + 4$$
$$2 \times 7 = \square \times (3 + 4)$$
$$2 \times 7 = \square \times 3 + \square \times 4$$
$$2 \times 7 = \square + \square$$
$$14 = \square$$

Answer the question.

3. Which number could replace the $\square$?

$$7 = 7$$
$$\square \times 7 = 7 \times 2$$

4. What is the value of m?

$$m \times 9 \times 8 = 9 \times 8 \times 5$$

Write the number that replaces the $\square$.

5.
$$10 = 10$$
$$4 \times 10 = 10 \times \square$$

6.
$$2 + 8 = 10$$
$$\square \times (2 + 8) = 5 \times 10$$

7.
$$9 + 9 = 18$$
$$(9 + 9) \times \square = 18 \times 3$$

8.
$$5 = 5$$
$$5 \times \square = 5 \times 10$$

Choose the answer.

9. Which number could replace the $\square$?

$$6 = 6$$
$$2 \times 6 = \square \times 6$$

A. 2   B. 6

C. 12   D. 36

10. What is the value of m?

$$m \times 4 \times 6 = 4 \times 6$$

A. 1   B. 3

C. 6   D. 24

© K12 Inc. All rights reserved.

T R Y   I T

11. Elias bought a bag of marbles. He wrote this equation to show the number of marbles in one bag.

$$n = 12$$

If Elias bought 3 bags of marbles, which equation would represent the number of marbles he has now?

A. $3 \times n = 4$

B. $3 \times n = 12$

C. $3 \times n = 15$

D. $3 \times n = 36$

12. Sandra bought a bunch of roses. She wrote this equation to show the number of roses in one bunch.

$$p = 10$$

If Sandra bought 5 bunches of roses, which equation would represent the number of roses she has now?

A. $5 \times p = 60$

B. $5 \times p = 50$

C. $5 \times p = 25$

D. $5 \times p = 15$

13. Which number could replace the ☐?

$$15 = 15$$
$$4 \times 15 = 15 \times \square$$

A. 4   B. 15

C. 60   D. 120

14. Which number could replace the ☐?

$$20 = 20$$
$$\square \times 20 = 20 \times 3$$

A. 3   B. 20

C. 80   D. 100

15. Laura bought 10 red apples last week. Ellen also bought 5 red apples and 5 yellow apples last week. Laura bought 4 times as many apples this week as she did last week. Ellen also bought 4 times as many apples this week as she did last week.

Which statement is true?

A. Ellen bought more apples than Laura.

B. Laura bought more apples than Ellen.

C. Laura and Ellen bought the same number of apples this week.

16. Dario bought 4 notepads last month. Mitch also bought 4 notepads last month. Dario bought 2 times as many notepads this month as he did last month. Mitch also bought 2 times as many notepads as he did last month.

Which statement is true?

A. Dario bought more notepads than Mitch.

B. Mitch and Dario bought the same number of notepads.

C. Mitch bought more notepads than Dario.

© K12 Inc. All rights reserved.

Two-Variable Equations (A)

Substitute and Solve

© K12 Inc. All rights reserved.

Worked Examples

For equations with two variables: If you know the value of one variable, you can find the value of the other variable.

PROBLEM 1 What is the value of n if $p = 5$?

$n = p + 3 + 11$

SOLUTION

$n = p + 3 + 11$

$n = 5 + 3 + 11$ ⟵   Substitute 5 for p.

$n = 19$ ⟵   Solve for n.

ANSWER The value of n is 19.

PROBLEM 2 What is the value of b if $c = 4$?

$b = 3 \times c + 9$

SOLUTION

$b = 3 \times c + 9$

$b = 3 \times 4 + 9$ ⟵   Substitute 4 for c.

$b = 21$ ⟵   Solve for b.

ANSWER The value of b is 21.

Solve.

1. What is the value of y if $x = 7$?
   $y = 16 - x$

2. If $t = 3$, what is the value of s?
   $s = 8 \times t + 1$

3. If $y = 9$, what is the value of n?
   $4 \times y - 5 = n$

4. What is the value of a if $b = 10$?
   $a = b \times 3 + 2$

5. If $c = 4$, what is the value of d?
   $c \times 2 + 5 = d$

6. What is the value of n if $p = 12$?
   $n = p - 5 - 7$

L E A R N

Line Segments in the Coordinate Plane

Horizontal Segment Lengths

⋯⋯ **Worked Examples**

If you know the coordinates of the endpoints of a horizontal line segment, you can use subtraction to find its length.

PROBLEM 1

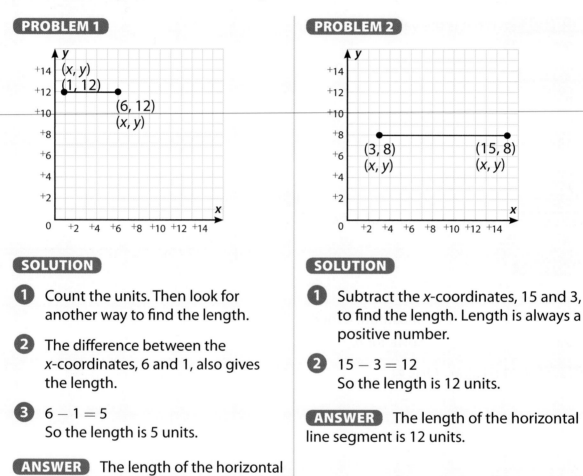

PROBLEM 2

SOLUTION

1 Count the units. Then look for another way to find the length.

2 The difference between the x-coordinates, 6 and 1, also gives the length.

3 $6 - 1 = 5$
So the length is 5 units.

ANSWER The length of the horizontal line segment is 5 units.

SOLUTION

1 Subtract the x-coordinates, 15 and 3, to find the length. Length is always a positive number.

2 $15 - 3 = 12$
So the length is 12 units.

ANSWER The length of the horizontal line segment is 12 units.

© K12 Inc. All rights reserved.

Subtract to find the length of the horizontal line segment.
Write the subtraction equation you used. Then write the length of the
segment in units.

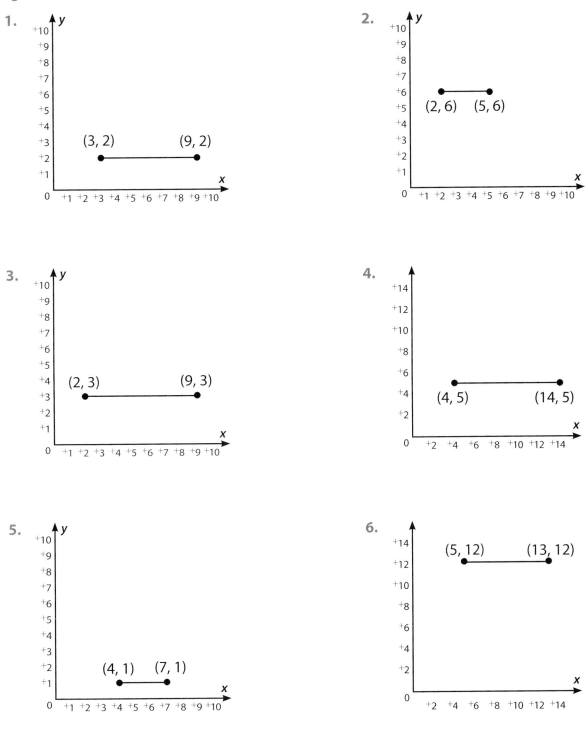

© K12 Inc. All rights reserved.

LINE SEGMENTS IN THE COORDINATE PLANE

L E A R N

Line Segments in the Coordinate Plane

Vertical Segment Lengths

Worked Examples

If you know the coordinates of the endpoints of a vertical line segment, you can use subtraction to find its length.

PROBLEM 1

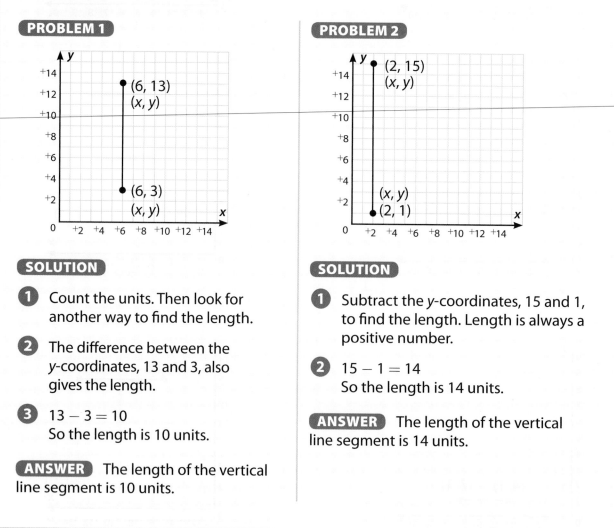

PROBLEM 2

SOLUTION

1 Count the units. Then look for another way to find the length.

2 The difference between the *y*-coordinates, 13 and 3, also gives the length.

3 $13 - 3 = 10$
So the length is 10 units.

ANSWER The length of the vertical line segment is 10 units.

SOLUTION

1 Subtract the *y*-coordinates, 15 and 1, to find the length. Length is always a positive number.

2 $15 - 1 = 14$
So the length is 14 units.

ANSWER The length of the vertical line segment is 14 units.

© K12 Inc. All rights reserved.

L E A R N

Subtract to find the length of the vertical line segment.
Write the subtraction equation you used. Then write the length of the
segment in units.

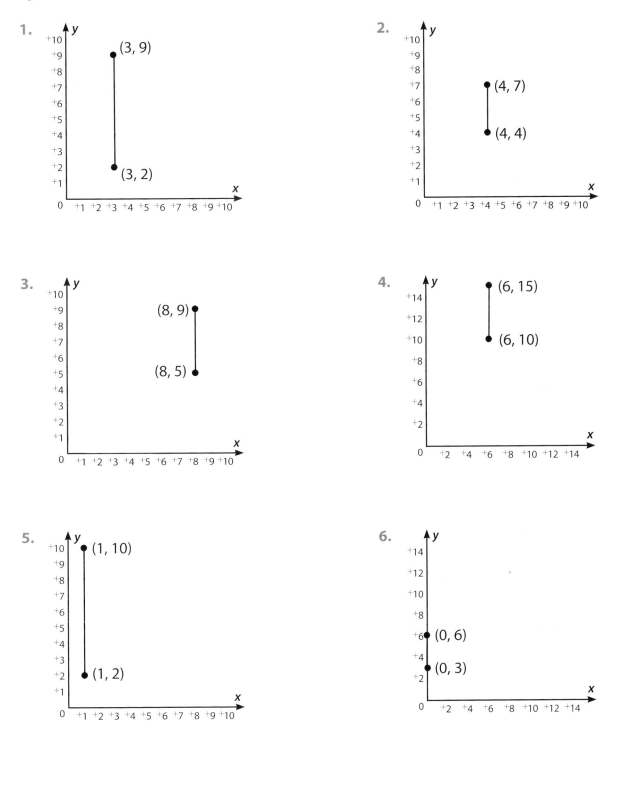

1.
(3, 9)
(3, 2)

2.
(4, 7)
(4, 4)

3.
(8, 9)
(8, 5)

4.
(6, 15)
(6, 10)

5.
(1, 10)
(1, 2)

6.
(0, 6)
(0, 3)

© K12 Inc. All rights reserved.

LEARN

Linear Relationships (A)

Points on a Line

Read the problem and follow the directions.

1. Write the ordered pairs to complete the table.

$y = 3 \times x$		
Input x	Output y	(Input, Output) (x, y)
0	0	?
+1	+3	?
+2	+6	?
+3	+9	?
+4	+12	?
+5	+15	?

2. Complete the input-output table and then plot the points on a coordinate grid.

Rule: Subtract 3		
Input x	Output y	Ordered Pair (x, y)
+3	0	?
+4	+1	?
+5	?	?
+6	?	?
+7	?	?
+8	?	?

© K12 Inc. All rights reserved.

T R Y   I T

Choose the answer.

3. Suketo plotted 3 points from the equation $y = 2 \times x$ on this coordinate grid. He drew a straight line through the points. Which ordered pair would also be on this line?

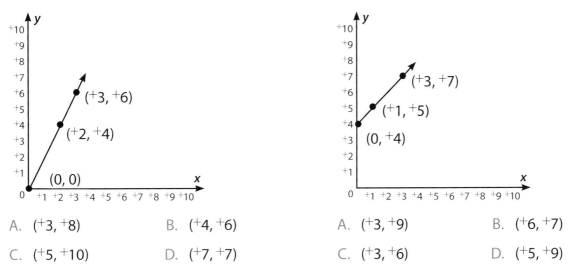

($^+3$, $^+6$)

($^+2$, $^+4$)

(0, 0)

A. ($^+3$, $^+8$)   B. ($^+4$, $^+6$)

C. ($^+5$, $^+10$)   D. ($^+7$, $^+7$)

4. Sari plotted 3 points from the equation $y = x + 4$ on this coordinate grid. She drew a straight line through the points. Which ordered pair would also be on this line?

($^+3$, $^+7$)

($^+1$, $^+5$)

(0, $^+4$)

A. ($^+3$, $^+9$)   B. ($^+6$, $^+7$)

C. ($^+3$, $^+6$)   D. ($^+5$, $^+9$)

5. Identify the graph that matches the equation in the table.

$y = x + 3$		
Input x	Output y	Ordered Pair (x, y)
0	$^+3$	(0, $^+3$)
$^+1$	$^+4$	($^+1$, $^+4$)
$^+2$	$^+5$	($^+2$, $^+5$)
$^+3$	$^+6$	($^+3$, $^+6$)
$^+4$	$^+7$	($^+4$, $^+7$)
$^+5$	$^+8$	($^+5$, $^+8$)

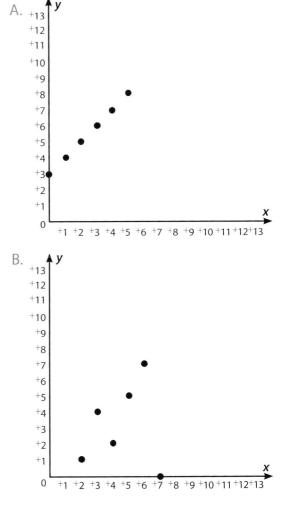

© K12 Inc. All rights reserved.

TRY IT

Linear Relationships (B)

More Straight Lines

Worked Examples

You can write ordered pairs (x, y) from an input-output table. Then you can graph the ordered pairs on a coordinate plane and see that they lie on a straight line.

PROBLEM Use the input and output values on the table to write ordered pairs in the third column. Then plot the points on the coordinate grid.

Plot the points on the coordinate grid.

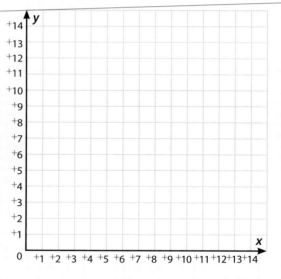

Rule: Subtract 5 or $y = x - 5$		
Input x	Output y	(Input, Output) (x, y)
+5	0	?
+6	+1	?
+7	+2	?
+8	+3	?
+9	+4	?
+10	+5	?
+11	+6	?
+12	+7	?
+13	+8	?

© K12 Inc. All rights reserved.

SOLUTION

1. To write the ordered pairs in the third column of the table, follow these steps:
   - Write the value of the *x*-coordinate given in the Input column on the same row.
   - Follow the *x*-coordinate with a comma, and skip a space.
   - Write the value of the *y*-coordinate from the Output column on the same row.
   - Enclose the coordinates with parentheses.

2. To plot the points on the coordinate grid, follow these steps:
   - To plot point (⁺5, 0), start at the origin and move right 5 units on the *x*-axis, in a positive direction. From that point, move 0 units on the *y*-axis, not moving up or down. Now draw a point.
   - To plot point (⁺6, ⁺1), start at the origin and move right 6 units on the *x*-axis, in a positive direction. From that point, move up 1 unit in a positive direction, parallel to the *y*-axis. Now draw a point.
   - Continue until all points have been plotted.

ANSWER

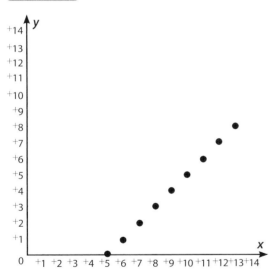

Rule: Subtract 5 or $y = x - 5$		
Input *x*	Output *y*	(Input, Output) (*x*, *y*)
⁺5	0	(⁺5, ⁺0)
⁺6	⁺1	(⁺6, ⁺1)
⁺7	⁺2	(⁺7, ⁺2)
⁺8	⁺3	(⁺8, ⁺3)
⁺9	⁺4	(⁺9, ⁺4)
⁺10	⁺5	(⁺10, ⁺5)
⁺11	⁺6	(⁺11, ⁺6)
⁺12	⁺7	(⁺12, ⁺7)
⁺13	⁺8	(⁺13, ⁺8)

© K12 Inc. All rights reserved.

Write the ordered pairs (x, y) to complete the table. Then plot the points on the coordinate grid.

1.

Rule: Add 3 or $y = x + 3$		
Input x	Output y	(Input, Output) (x, y)
0	+3	?
+1	+4	?
+2	+5	?
+3	+6	?
+4	+7	?
+5	+8	?
+6	+9	?
+7	+10	?
+8	+11	?

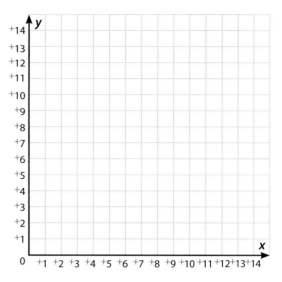

2.

Rule: Subtract 4 or $y = x - 4$		
Input x	Output y	(Input, Output) (x, y)
+14	+10	?
+13	+9	?
+12	+8	?
+11	+7	?
+10	+6	?
+9	+5	?
+8	+4	?
+7	+3	?

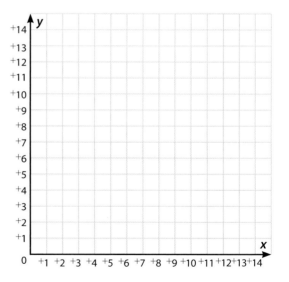

© K12 Inc. All rights reserved.

LEARN

ALGEBRA THINKING

LINEAR RELATIONSHIPS (B)

Read the problem and complete the table. (Use the input values and apply the rule given in the table to write the output values in the second column and the ordered pairs in the third column.) Then plot the points on the coordinate grid.

3. Serena attended camp. The number of new friends she made each day was 2 more than the number of days she was there. So on Day 4, Serena made 4 + 2, or 6, new friends. Help Serena complete the table and plot the ordered pairs of (day, new friends) on the coordinate grid.

Rule: Add 2 or $y = x + 2$		
Input x	Output y	(Input, Output) (x, y)
+4	?	?
+5	?	?
+6	?	?
+7	?	?
+8	?	?
+9	?	?
+10	?	?
+11	?	?

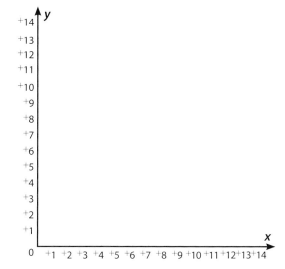

© K12 Inc. All rights reserved.

LEARN

Linear Relationships (B)

Check the Coordinates

Read the problem and follow the directions.

1. Write the ordered pairs to complete the table.

y = x − 10		
Input **x**	**Output** **y**	**(Input, Output)** **(x, y)**
⁺20	⁺10	?
⁺19	⁺9	?
⁺18	⁺8	?
⁺17	⁺7	?
⁺16	⁺6	?
⁺15	⁺5	?
⁺14	⁺4	?

Choose the answer.

2. Joyce plotted 3 points from the equation $y = 3 \times x$ on this coordinate grid. She drew a straight line through the points. Which ordered pair would also be on this line?

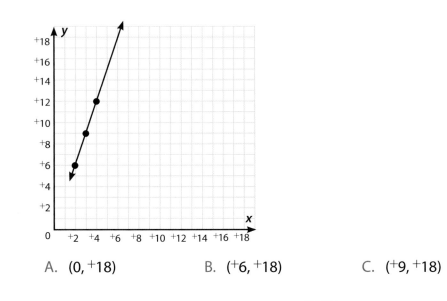

A. (0, ⁺18)   B. (⁺6, ⁺18)   C. (⁺9, ⁺18)   D. (⁺6, ⁺6)

© K12 Inc. All rights reserved.

TRY IT

3. Identify the graph that matches the equation in the table.

y = x − 7		
Input x	Output y	(Input, Output) (x, y)
+12	+5	?
+11	+4	?
+10	+3	?
+9	+2	?
+8	+1	?
+7	0	?

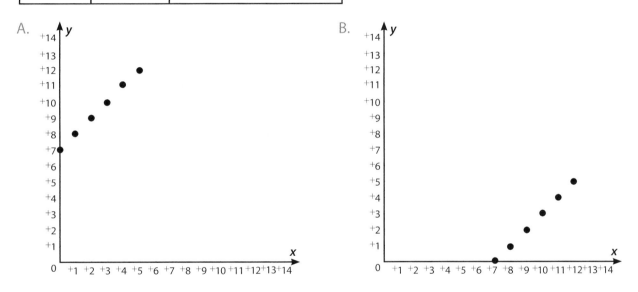

A.

B.

© K12 Inc. All rights reserved.

TRY IT

4. Which correctly graphs $y = x - 8$?

A.

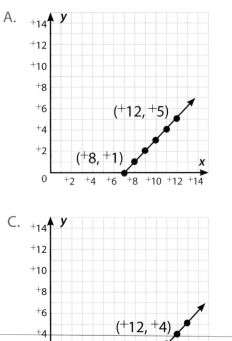

$(+12, +5)$

$(+8, +1)$

B.

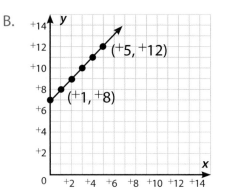

$(+5, +12)$

$(+1, +8)$

C.

$(+12, +4)$

$(+9, +1)$

5. Which correctly graphs $y = x - 9$?

A.

$(+14, +6)$

$(+10, +2)$

B.

$(+14, +5)$

$(+10, +1)$

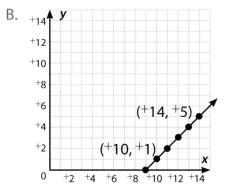

C.

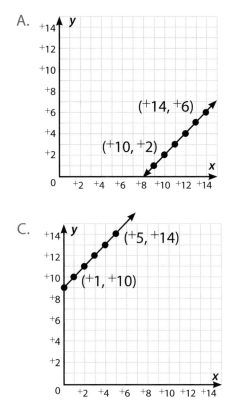

$(+5, +14)$

$(+1, +10)$

© K12 Inc. All rights reserved.

TRY IT

6. Parker plotted 3 points from the equation $y = x + 3$ on this coordinate grid. He drew a straight line through the points. Which ordered pair would also be on this line?

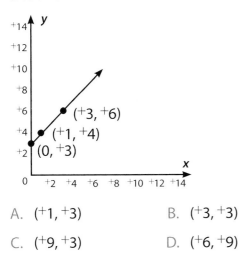

A. $(^+1, ^+3)$ B. $(^+3, ^+3)$

C. $(^+9, ^+3)$ D. $(^+6, ^+9)$

7. Jen plotted 3 points from the equation $y = 3 \times x + 1$ on this coordinate grid. She drew a straight line through the points. Which ordered pair would also be on this line?

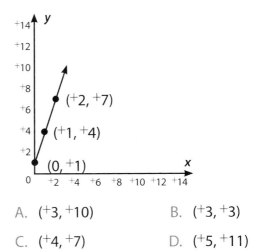

A. $(^+3, ^+10)$ B. $(^+3, ^+3)$

C. $(^+4, ^+7)$ D. $(^+5, ^+11)$

© K12 Inc. All rights reserved.

TRY IT

Perimeters of Polygons

Measure Perimeter

Worked Examples

You can use a ruler to find the perimeter of a polygon. First you measure each side of the outside border of the figure. Be sure to measure with the unit mentioned in the problem, centimeter or inch. Then you find the sum of the lengths of the sides and include the unit in your answer.

PROBLEM Use a dual-scale ruler to find the perimeter of this figure in centimeters.

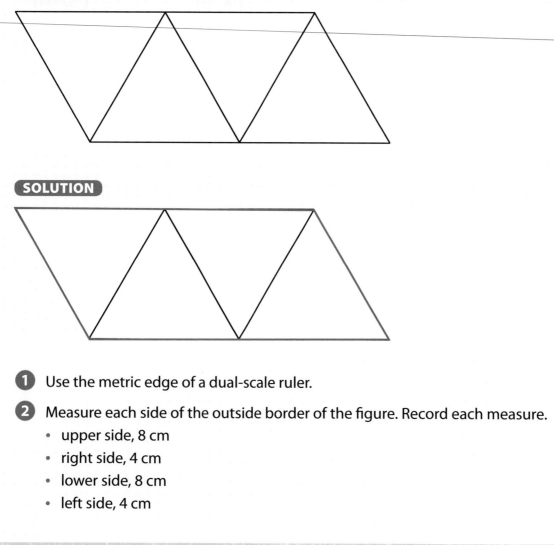

SOLUTION

1. Use the metric edge of a dual-scale ruler.

2. Measure each side of the outside border of the figure. Record each measure.
   - upper side, 8 cm
   - right side, 4 cm
   - lower side, 8 cm
   - left side, 4 cm

© K12 Inc. All rights reserved.

L E A R N

3 Find the sum of the lengths of the sides.

ANSWER The perimeter of the figure is 24 cm.

Use a dual-scale ruler to solve.

1. What is the perimeter of this figure in centimeters?

2. What is the perimeter of this figure in inches?

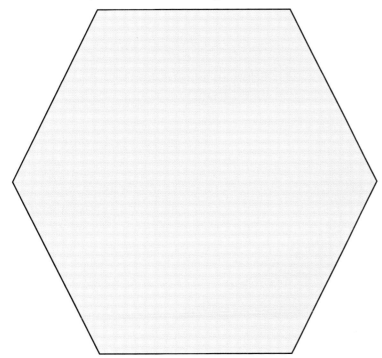

© K12 Inc. All rights reserved.

L E A R N

3. What is the perimeter of this figure in centimeters?

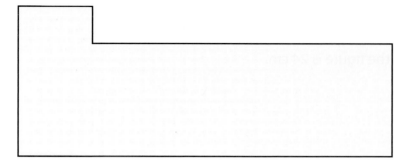

4. What is the perimeter of this figure in inches?

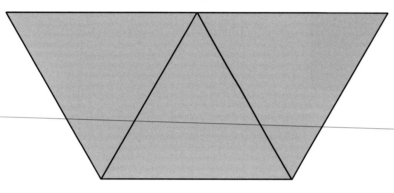

5. What is the perimeter of the shaded part of this figure in centimeters?

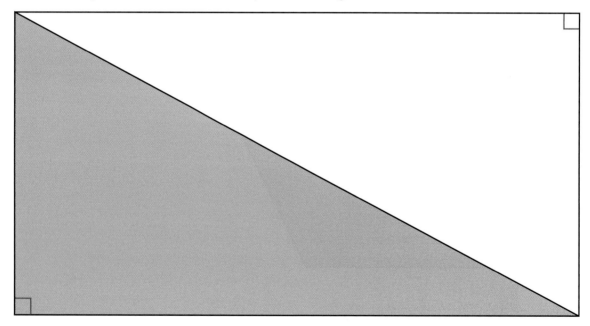

© K12 Inc. All rights reserved.

LEARN

Perimeters of Polygons

Perimeter Practice

Use a ruler to find the perimeter of the figure in centimeters.

1.

2.

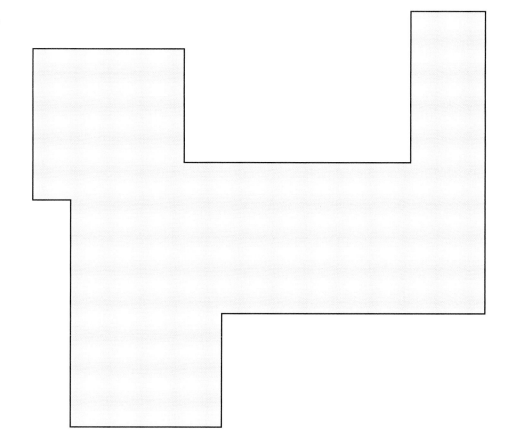

© K12 Inc. All rights reserved.

T R Y   I T

Use a ruler to find the perimeter of the figure in inches.

3.

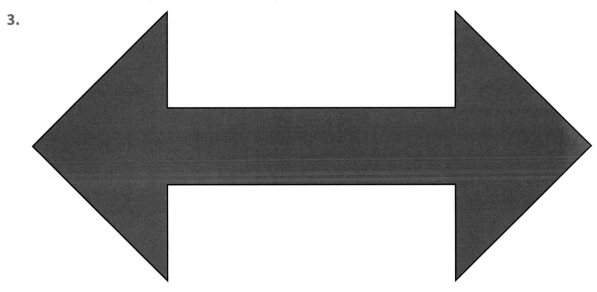

Solve.

4. The rectangle and the hexagon have the same perimeter.
What are the lengths of the sides of the rectangle that are unmarked?

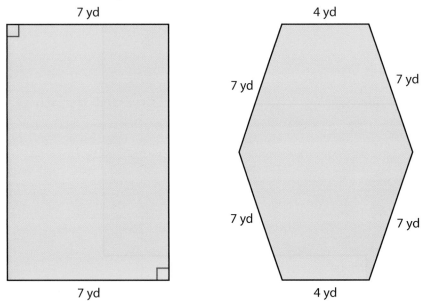

7 yd

7 yd

4 yd

7 yd   7 yd

7 yd   7 yd

4 yd

5. What is the perimeter of this parallelogram?

13 in.

5 in.   5 in.

13 in.

© K12 Inc. All rights reserved.

TRY IT

Choose the answer.

6. The length of one side of the square is equal to the length of 6 arrows. If each arrow represents 1 unit, what is the perimeter of the square?

A. 6 units   B. 18 units

C. 24 units   D. 36 units

7. What is the perimeter of the shaded rectangle on this grid?

A. 13 units   B. 14 units

C. 26 units   D. 28 units

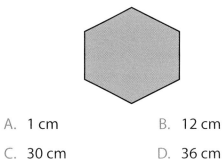

8. What is the perimeter of this polygon?

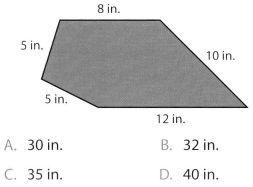

A. 30 in.   B. 32 in.

C. 35 in.   D. 40 in.

9. What is the perimeter of the polygon if each side is 6 cm?

A. 1 cm   B. 12 cm

C. 30 cm   D. 36 cm

10. The base of Jill's house is in the shape of a regular octagon. Each side of the octagon measures 25 feet. Find the perimeter of the base of Jill's house.

A. 100 ft   B. 150 ft

C. 200 ft   D. 250 ft

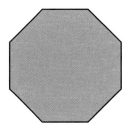

© K12 Inc. All rights reserved.

TRY IT

11. Which triangle has the same perimeter as the green triangle?

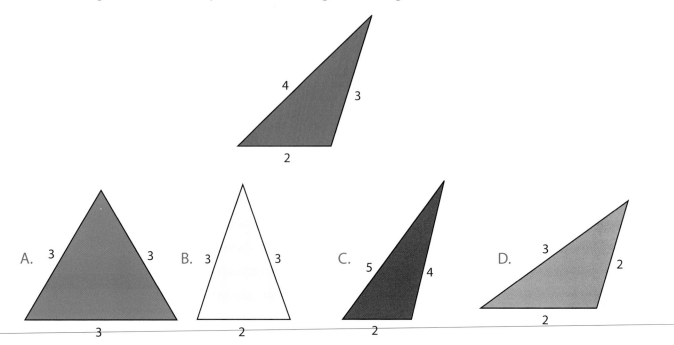

A. 3   3   3

B. 3   3   2

C. 5   4   2

D. 3   2   2

12. The triangle has the same perimeter as the square.

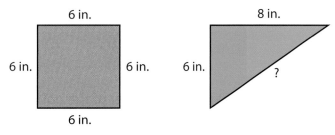

6 in.

6 in.   6 in.

6 in.

8 in.

6 in.   ?

What is the length of the unknown side of the triangle?

A. 6 in.   B. 10 in.   C. 14 in.   D. 24 in.

13. All angles shown on the figure are right angles.

What is the perimeter of the figure?

A. 16 ft

B. 18 ft

C. 20 ft

D. 22 ft

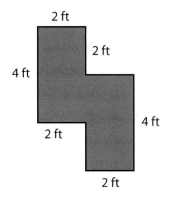

2 ft

2 ft

4 ft

4 ft

2 ft

2 ft

© K12 Inc. All rights reserved.

T R Y   I T

14. Michele is looking for a rug with a perimeter of 24 feet.

Which rectangular rug has a perimeter of 24 feet?

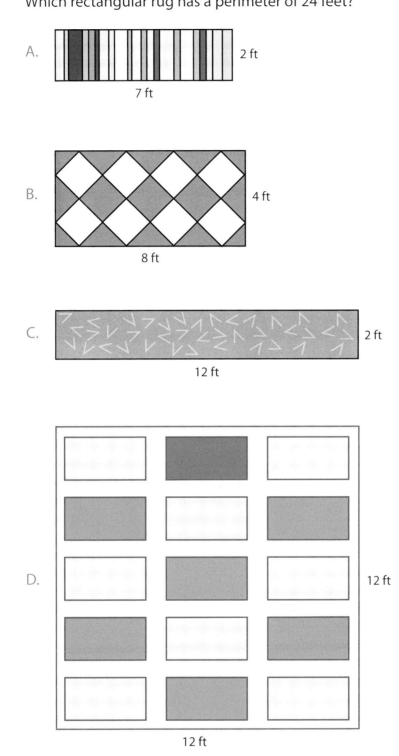

A.   2 ft
7 ft

B.   4 ft
8 ft

C.   2 ft
12 ft

D.   12 ft
12 ft

© K12 Inc. All rights reserved.

TRY IT

Formulas for Perimeter (A)

Find the Perimeters

Solve.

1. What is the perimeter of this rectangle?

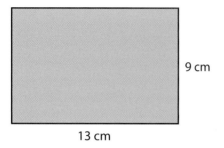

9 cm

13 cm

2. What is the perimeter of this rectangle?

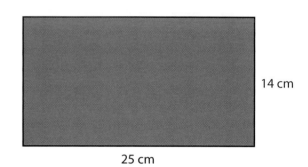

14 cm

25 cm

3. What is the perimeter of this square?

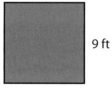

9 ft

4. What is the perimeter of this square?

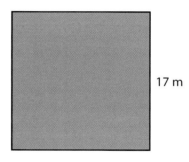

17 m

5. Chuck wants to put a fence around his square garden. One side of his garden measures 3 meters. How much fence will Chuck need?

Find the perimeter. Use a formula, or equation, if you wish.
Note: Diagrams are not drawn to scale.

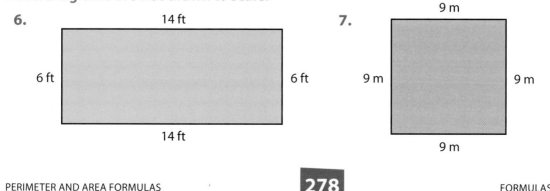

6.

14 ft

6 ft   6 ft

14 ft

7.

9 m

9 m   9 m

9 m

© K12 Inc. All rights reserved.

T R Y   I T

8.

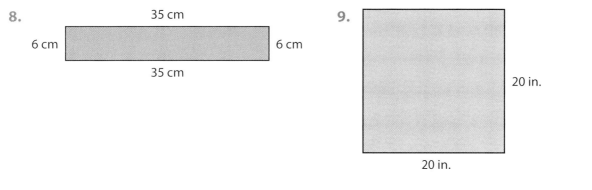

35 cm

6 cm   6 cm

35 cm

9.

20 in.

20 in.

Choose the answer.

10. Jordan needs to find the perimeter of a large rectangular table represented by the sketch. Which statement describes how she could correctly calculate the perimeter?

9 units

3 units   3 units

9 units

    A. Add $9 + 3$.

    B. Multiply 9×3.

    C. Add $9 + 9 + 3 + 3$.

    D. Multiply $9 \times 9 \times 3 \times 3$.

11. Mrs. Vasquez needs to determine the perimeter of the rectangular window shown so she can buy wood trim to go around it.

30 in.

48 in.

    Which equation could Mrs. Vasquez use to determine the perimeter of the window?

    A. $P = 48 \times 30$

    B. $P = 48 + 30$

    C. $P = 48 + 30 + 48$

    D. $P = 48 + 48 + 30 + 30$

12. What is the perimeter of the rectangle?

    A. 11 ft

    B. 20 ft

    C. 22 ft

    D. 28 ft

4 ft

7 ft

© K12 Inc. All rights reserved.

TRY IT

13. Aldo folded a paper in half, then he cut out a rectangle along the fold. What is the perimeter of the cut rectangle when it is unfolded?

A. 5 in.

B. 7 in.

C. 10 in.

D. 14 in.

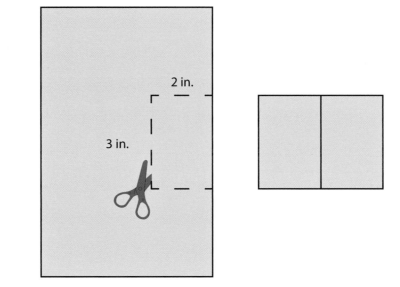

14. Mrs. Anderson wants to install a fence around her square yard. One side of the yard measures 36 feet. How much feet of fencing does she need?

A. 72 ft

B. 144 ft

C. 288 ft

D. 1,296 ft

Read the problem and follow the directions.

15. Maria used this formula to find the perimeter of a rectangular game board:

$(2 \times 5) + (2 \times 8) = 26$; Perimeter is 26 inches.

Sketch and label Maria's game board. Then write another equation that you can use to find the perimeter of the game board.

© K12 Inc. All rights reserved.

TRY IT

Worked Examples

You can use formulas to find the perimeter of geometric shapes. First you draw and label a diagram. Then you write a formula and replace the variables with the dimensions from the diagram. Next you compute the perimeter.

PROBLEM What is the perimeter of a rectangular picture frame with these dimensions?

9 in.

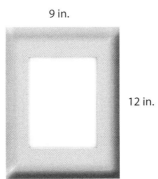

12 in.

SOLUTION 1

Add the lengths of the sides to find the perimeter of a rectangle.

$P = l + l + w + w$
$P = 12 + 12 + 9 + 9$
$P = 42$

ANSWER The perimeter of the picture frame is 42 inches.

SOLUTION 2

Add (2 × length) + (2 × width) to find the perimeter of a rectangle.

$P = (2 \times l) + (2 \times w)$
$P = (2 \times 12) + (2 \times 9)$
$P = 24 + 18$
$P = 42$

ANSWER The perimeter of the picture frame is 42 inches.

© K12 Inc. All rights reserved.

Complete the equation to find the perimeter of the figure.

1.
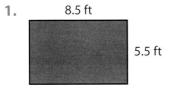

8.5 ft

5.5 ft

$P = l + w + l + w$
$P = \underline{?} + 5.5 + 8.5 + \underline{?}$
$P = \underline{?}$

The perimeter is $\underline{?}$ feet.

L E A R N

Write a perimeter formula for the figure. Replace the variables in your formula with the corresponding given measures. Then find the perimeter.

2. The rectangle below has a width of 5 centimeters and a length of 22 centimeters.

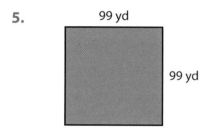

3.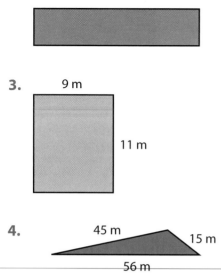

   9 m

   11 m

4. 45 m

   15 m

   56 m

5. 99 yd

   99 yd

Solve.

6. Trudy sewed together two quilt squares like the ones shown. She then put fringe around the outside of the new rectangular piece of material. How many inches of fringe did Trudy use?

   13 in.

   13 in.   13 in.

   13 in.

   13 in.

   13 in.   13 in.

   13 in.

7. Stephen folds a piece of cardboard and then cuts out a triangle as shown. What is the perimeter of the triangular piece of cardboard?

   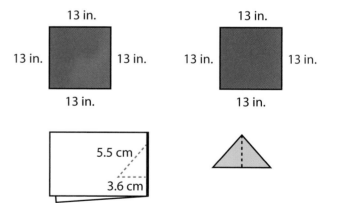

   5.5 cm

   3.6 cm

© K12 Inc. All rights reserved.

LEARN

Worked Examples

You can use formulas to find the perimeter of geometric shapes. First you draw and label a diagram. Then you write a formula and replace the variables with the dimensions from the diagram. Next you compute the perimeter.

PROBLEM Karl wants to put a fence around a rectangular garden that is 6 feet by 9 feet. How long should the fence be?

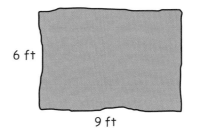

6 ft

9 ft

SOLUTION 1

1 Draw and label a diagram.

2 Use the perimeter formula
$P = (2 \times l) + (2 \times w)$.

$P = (2 \times l) + (2 \times w)$
$P = (2 \times 9) + (2 \times 6)$
$P = 18 + 12$
$P = 30$

ANSWER The perimeter is 30 ft, so the fence will be 30 ft long.

SOLUTION 2

1 Draw and label a diagram.

2 Use the perimeter formula
$P = 2 \times (l + w)$.

$P = 2 \times (l + w)$
$P = 2 \times (9 + 6)$
$P = 2 \times 15$
$P = 30$

ANSWER The perimeter is 30 ft, so the fence will be 30 ft long.

Complete the equation to solve.

8. A swimming pool is a rectangle 100 feet long and 45 feet wide. What is the perimeter of the pool?

$P = (2 \times l) + (2 \times w)$

$P = (2 \times \underline{\ ?\ }) + (2 \times \underline{\ ?\ })$

$P = \underline{\ ?\ } + \underline{\ ?\ }$

$P = \underline{\ ?\ }$

The perimeter of the pool is $\underline{\ ?\ }$ ft.

Use a formula or equation to solve. Show your work.

9. A park is shaped like a square with sides that are 5.3 kilometers long. What is the length of a bike path that goes around the outside border of the park?

10. Jessica's bedroom is 4.6 meters long and 3 meters wide. She puts a wallpaper border around the perimeter of the room near the ceiling. How long is the wallpaper border?

© K12 Inc. All rights reserved.

L E A R N

Formulas for Perimeter (B)

Solve with Perimeter Formulas

Use a formula, or equation, to find the perimeter. Show your work.
Write the answer with the correct unit.

1.

12.25 m

1.5 m

2. Charlie builds a sandbox for his grandson. It is a square with sides
5 feet long. What is the perimeter of the sandbox?

Read the problem and follow the directions.

3. Mr. Tunison is building a house. Part of the floor plan for the house is
shown. Mr. Tunison is going to put carpet tape under the carpet
around the sides of Room A and under the carpet around the hallway.
How many feet of carpet tape does Mr. Tunison need? Show how to use
formulas to find the answer.

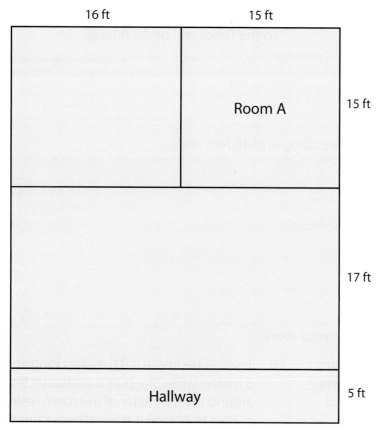

16 ft   15 ft

Room A   15 ft

17 ft

Hallway   5 ft

284

© K12 Inc. All rights reserved.

T R Y   I T

4. Find the missing measurements. Then find the perimeter.
Explain how you got your answer.

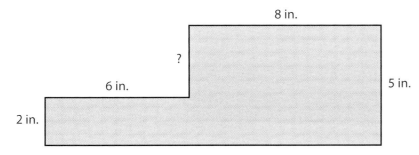

Choose the answer.

5. Mrs. Collins has two connected rectangular pens for her farm animals. The pens are shown below. She wants to surround the pair of pens with new fence, but she does not want to put a new fence between the pens.

6 yd

8 yd   15 yd

What should Mrs. Collins do to find the total length of fencing needed to surround the pair of pens?

A. Add all the numbers shown in the drawing.

B. Find the perimeter of the smaller pen, and then add 21.

C. Add the perimeters of the pens, and then subtract 12.

D. Add the numbers shown in the drawing, and then multiply by 2.

6. What is the perimeter of the swimming pool?

A. 50 ft

B. 100 ft

C. 200 ft

D. 600 ft

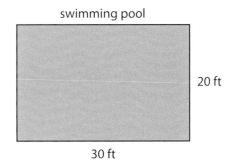

swimming pool

20 ft

30 ft

© K12 Inc. All rights reserved.

TRY IT

7. Ron installed wallpaper border around the top of his bedroom. If the rectangular bedroom measures 12 feet by 14 feet, how many feet of border did he use?

   A. 26 ft   B. 48 ft   C. 52 ft   D. 56 ft

8. Tirey has a pool that measures 48 meters long and 15 meters wide. What is the perimeter of the pool?

   A. 63 m

   B. 96 m

   C. 116 m

   D. 126 m

9. Damon built a dog house. The base was a perfect square that was 6 feet long on each side. What was the perimeter of the dog house?

   A. 12 ft

   B. 18 ft

   C. 24 ft

   D. 36 ft

10. Manuella compared the perimeter of the figures below.

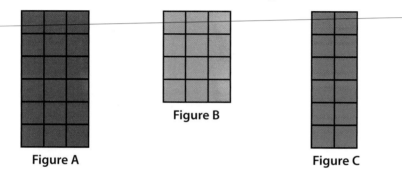

Figure B

Figure A   Figure C

Which sentence is true?

   A. The perimeter of Figure B is less than the perimeter of Figure A.

   B. The perimeter of Figure C is greater than the perimeter of Figure A.

   C. The perimeter of Figure A is less than the perimeter of Figure C.

   D. The perimeter of Figure A is equal to the perimeter of Figure C.

11. Which equation would **not** correctly calculate the perimeter of this rectangle?

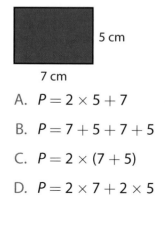

5 cm

7 cm

   A. $P = 2 \times 5 + 7$

   B. $P = 7 + 5 + 7 + 5$

   C. $P = 2 \times (7 + 5)$

   D. $P = 2 \times 7 + 2 \times 5$

12. Which **two** equations could be used to calculate the perimeter of this square?

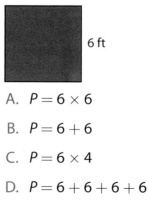

6 ft

   A. $P = 6 \times 6$

   B. $P = 6 + 6$

   C. $P = 6 \times 4$

   D. $P = 6 + 6 + 6 + 6$

© K12 Inc. All rights reserved.

TRY IT

13. Terrence compared the perimeters of the shaded figures below.

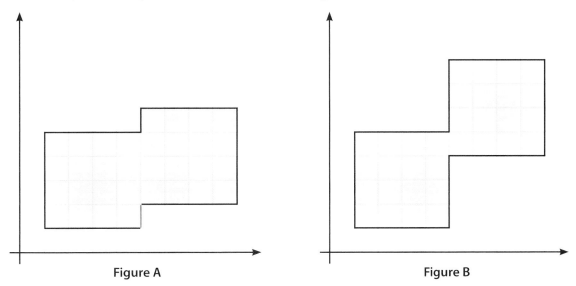

Figure A   Figure B

Which sentence is true?

A. The perimeter of Figure A is greater than the perimeter of Figure B.

B. The perimeter of Figure A is less than the perimeter of Figure B.

14. Which statement about these rectangles is true?

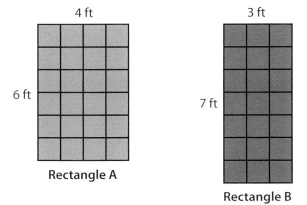

A. The perimeter of Rectangle A is greater than the perimeter of Rectangle B.

B. The perimeter of Rectangle A is the same as the perimeter of Rectangle B.

C. The area of Rectangle A is the same as the area of Rectangle B.

D. The area of Rectangle B is greater than the area of Rectangle A.

© K12 Inc. All rights reserved.

T R Y   I T

Formulas for Area (A)

Solve with Area Formulas

Use a formula, or equation, to find the area. Show your work.

1.

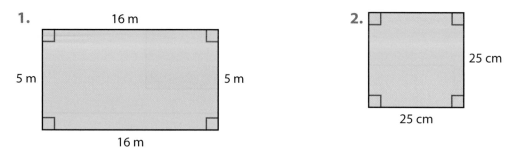

16 m

5 m   5 m

16 m

2.

25 cm

25 cm

3. Find the area of a rectangle that is 21 yards long by 9 yards wide.

Solve.

4. Briana helps her mother make a quilt. The quilt is 6 feet wide and 12 feet long. What is the area of the quilt?

5. Use formulas to find the area of the compound figure. Show your work. Explain how you found your answer.

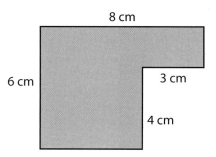

8 cm

6 cm   3 cm

4 cm

6. What is the area of this rectangle?

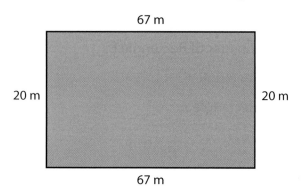

67 m

20 m   20 m

67 m

T R Y   I T

© K12 Inc. All rights reserved.

Choose the answer.

7. Shawn drew a diagram showing the dimensions of his closet and Emma's closet.

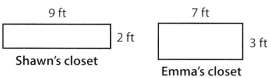

9 ft

7 ft

2 ft

3 ft

Shawn's closet

Emma's closet

Which statement about the closets is true?

A. Emma's closet has a greater perimeter and area.

B. Shawn's closet has a greater perimeter and area.

C. Emma's closet has a greater area but a smaller perimeter.

D. Shawn's closet has a greater area but a smaller perimeter.

8. Jennifer measured a rectangular garden in her backyard. The plot is shown.

9 ft

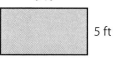

5 ft

Which sentence gives the correct area and perimeter of Jennifer's garden?

A. The area is 14 ft^2 and the perimeter is 28 ft.

B. The area is 28 ft^2 and the perimeter is 45 ft.

C. The area is 45 ft^2 and the perimeter is 14 ft.

D. The area is 45 ft^2 and the perimeter is 28 ft.

9. Justice measured his rectangular vegetable garden.

3 m

5 m

Which statement is true about the area and perimeter of Justice's garden?

A. The perimeter is 8 m and the area is 15 m^2.

B. The perimeter is 16 m and the area is 15 m^2.

C. The perimeter is 15 m and the area is 16 m^2.

D. The perimeter is 16 m and the area is 8 m^2.

10. On the grid, the shaded squares represent Nancy's closet floor.

Nancy says the perimeter of the closet floor is 22 units and the area is 24 square units. Which sentence best explains if she is correct, and why or why not?

A. Yes, she is correct because the area of a floor is always greater than its perimeter.

B. Yes, she is correct because 24 is the number of squares needed to cover the surface, and 22 is the sum of all the sides.

C. No, she is incorrect because 22 is the number of squares needed to cover the surface, and 24 is the sum of all the sides.

D. No, she is incorrect because the perimeter of a floor is always greater than its area.

© K12 Inc. All rights reserved.

T R Y   I T

11. Which rectangle has an area smaller than the one shown here?

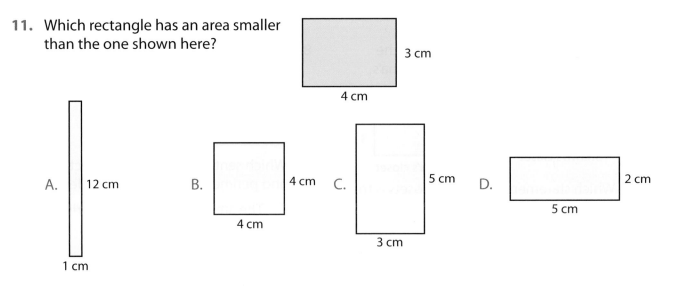

3 cm

4 cm

A. 12 cm 1 cm

B. 4 cm 4 cm

C. 5 cm 3 cm

D. 2 cm 5 cm

12. The dimensions of a rectangular tablecloth are shown below.

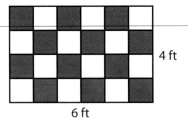

4 ft

6 ft

Which computation could be used to determine the area of the tablecloth?

A. Multiply 6 by 4.

B. Add 6 and 4.

C. Multiply 6 by 4, and then multiply by 2.

D. Add 6 and 4, and then multiply by 2.

13. Yolanda wants to water the grass in her rectangular backyard. Below is a diagram of the backyard.

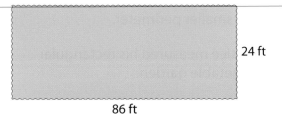

24 ft

86 ft

What is the area of Yolanda's backyard?

A. 220 ft²

B. 516 ft²

C. 1,884 ft²

D. 2,064 ft²

14. What is the area of the figure below?

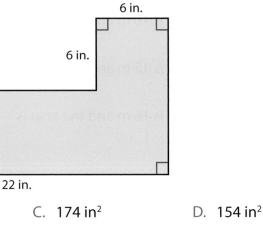

6 in.

6 in.

7 in.

22 in.

A. 252 in²   B. 190 in²   C. 174 in²   D. 154 in²

© K12 Inc. All rights reserved.

TRY IT

Formulas for Area (B)

Area of Complex Figures

Worked Examples

You can use area formulas to find the area of a complex figure. First you divide the figure into smaller rectangles or squares. Then you use formulas to find the area of the smaller figures. Next you find the sum of the areas.

PROBLEM Madeline wants to paste a flat piece of plastic to the front of the project display board shown. All angles are right angles. How many square inches of plastic does Madeline need?

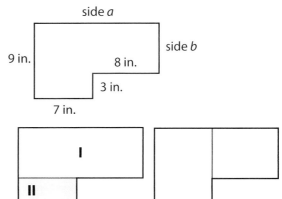

SOLUTION

1 Divide the figure into smaller rectangles or squares. Two ways to divide the figure are shown shown here. This solution is for the shaded figure on the left.

2 Use the given dimensions to find the dimensions that are not given.

3 Find the area of each rectangle.

Rectangle I	Rectangle II
$A = l \times w$	$A = l \times w$
$A = 15$ in. $\times 6$ in.	$A = 7$ in. $\times 3$ in.
$A = 90$ in^2	$A = 21$ in^2

4 Add the areas of the two rectangles to find the total area.
90 in$^2 + 21$ in$^2 = 111$ in^2

side a
- The 7 in. side and the 8 in. side, together, are the same length as side a.
- Add $7 + 8 = 15$.
- The length of side a is 15 in.
- Let 15 in. be the length of Rectangle I.

side b
- The lengths of side b and the 3 in. side together are the same length as the 9 in. side. So 9 in. minus 3 in. is the length of side b.
- Subtract $9 - 3 = 6$.
- The length of side b is 6 in.
- Let 6 in. be the width of Rectangle I.

ANSWER Madeline needs 111 in^2 of plastic to cover the front of the project display board.

© K12 Inc. All rights reserved.

L E A R N

Find the area. Show your work.

1.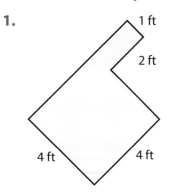

1 ft

2 ft

4 ft   4 ft

Rectangle	Square
$A = ? \times ?$	$A = ? \times ?$
$A = ? \times ?$	$A = ? \times ?$
$A = ?$	$A = ?$

Total area $= ?$ ft$^2 + ?$ ft$^2 = ?$ ft^2

2. The pyramid El Castillo stands in the Yucatan peninsula of Mexico. It has a square base with four staircases that jut out, one on each side. Joe drew an outline of a complex figure like the El Castillo pyramid. The dimensions are approximate. Use Joe's diagram to find the approximate total area that the base of the pyramid covers.

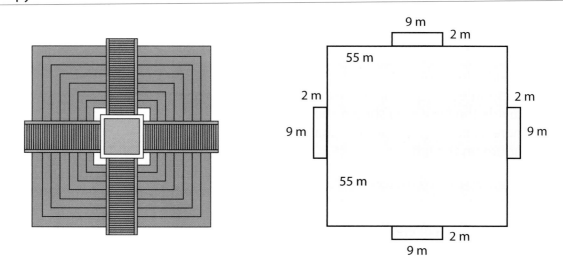

9 m
2 m
55 m
2 m   2 m
9 m   9 m
55 m
2 m
9 m

Square	Rectangle
$A = ? \times ?$	$A = ? \times ?$
$A = ?$	$A = ?$

The total area $= ?$ m$^2 + (4 \times ?$ m$^2)$

$= ?$ m$^2 + ?$ m^2

$= ?$ m^2

© K12 Inc. All rights reserved.

LEARN

Formulas for Area (B)

Interpret and Use Formulas

Find the perimeter and area of the figure. Explain how you found your answer.

1.

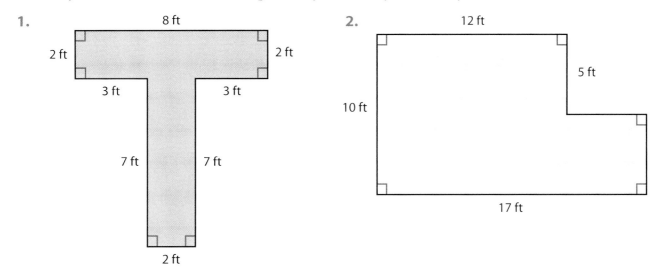

8 ft

2 ft   2 ft

3 ft   3 ft

7 ft   7 ft

2 ft

2.

12 ft

5 ft

10 ft

17 ft

Use Problems 1 and 2 to solve.

3. Which has the greater area?

4. Which has the lesser perimeter?

Solve. Explain how you found your answer.

5. The plastic flag on the mailbox at Janine's house is shown. Find the area of the entire figure.

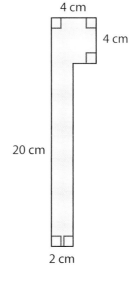

4 cm

4 cm

20 cm

2 cm

Solve.

6. What is the area of a rectangular field which is 25 meters long and 15 meters wide?

7. What is the area of a square if one side is 14 centimeters long?

© K12 Inc. All rights reserved.

T R Y   I T

Choose the answer.

8. A rectangle is 32 meters long and 4 meters wide. Which equation represents the area (A) of the rectangle?

A. $A = 32 \times 4$

B. $32 = (4 \times A) \times 4$

C. $32 = A \times 4$

D. $A = (2 \times 4) + (2 \times 32)$

9. Which rectangle has an area greater than the one shown?

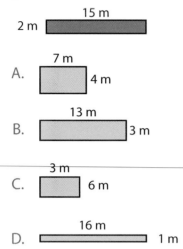

A.

B.

C.

D.

10. Which figure has an area greater than the one shown?

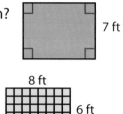

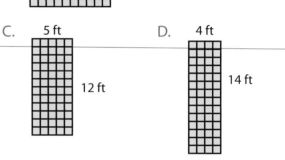

A.

B.

C.

D.

11. What is the area of the figure?

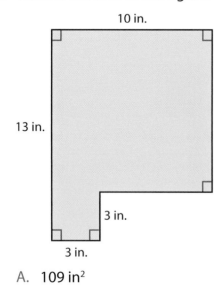

A. 109 in²

B. 100 in²

C. 90 in²

D. 46 in²

12. What is the area of the figure?

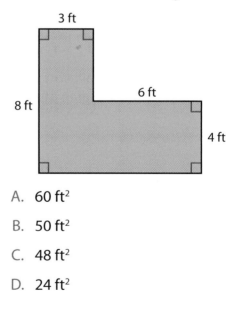

A. 60 ft²

B. 50 ft²

C. 48 ft²

D. 24 ft²

© K12 Inc. All rights reserved.

TRY IT

13. What is the area of the figure?

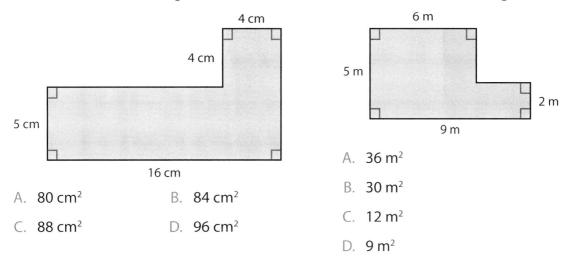

4 cm

4 cm

5 cm

16 cm

A. 80 cm²   B. 84 cm²

C. 88 cm²   D. 96 cm²

14. What is the area of the figure?

6 m

5 m

2 m

9 m

A. 36 m²

B. 30 m²

C. 12 m²

D. 9 m²

15. Mr. McBean is fencing a rectangular pasture for his horses. What is the area of the pasture that will be used for Mr. McBean's horses?

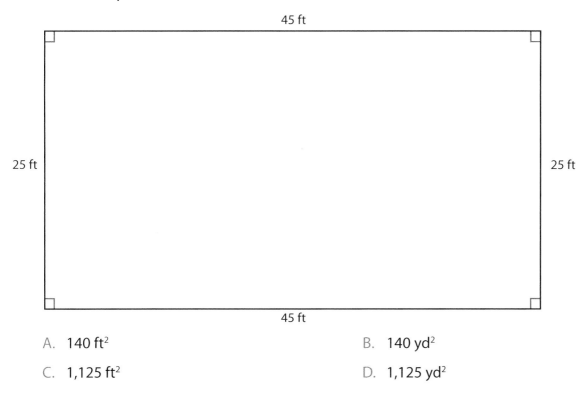

45 ft

25 ft   25 ft

45 ft

A. 140 ft²   B. 140 yd²

C. 1,125 ft²   D. 1,125 yd²

© K12 Inc. All rights reserved.

T R Y I T

Compare Area and Perimeter

Same Perimeter, Different Areas

You can use 1-inch square tiles to build rectangles or squares with the same perimeter but different areas. You can also use 1-inch grid paper to draw rectangles or squares with the same perimeter but different areas. Then you can enter your data in a table to compare the areas of these shapes.

PROBLEM Build or draw rectangles or squares that each has a perimeter of 14 inches. Use the table to help you write the dimensions of each shape. Then write the area of each shape.

Same Perimeter, Different Areas				
Name of shape	Length (*l*)	Width (*w*)	Area (*A*)	Perimeter (*P*)
Shape 1	$l = ?$ in.	$w = ?$ in.	$A = ?$ in^2	$P = 14$ in.
Shape 2	$l = ?$ in.	$w = ?$ in.	$A = ?$ in^2	$P = 14$ in.
Shape 3	$l = ?$ in.	$w = ?$ in.	$A = ?$ in^2	$P = 14$ in.

SOLUTION

1. Use the guess-and-test method of problem solving. Estimate how many tiles it will take to build a rectangle or square that has a perimeter of 14 inches. Count out the tiles and build a rectangle or square. You can also draw a rectangle or square on grid paper.

2. Starting at one corner of your shape, count the 1-inch lengths that form a border completely around the shape, or the perimeter of the shape.

3. If the perimeter of your shape is less than 14 inches, add 1 or more tiles. If the perimeter of your shape is greater than 14 inches, take away 1 or more tiles. Continue this process until you build a rectangle or square with a perimeter of 14 inches.

4. Record the dimensions of your first shape.

5. Count the 1-inch square tiles that make up the shape, or the area of the shape. You may also use the formula $A = l \times w$ or the formula $A = s \times s$. Record the area of the shape.

6. Continue to build rectangles that each have a 14-inch perimeter. The dimensions must be different for each shape.

© K12 Inc. All rights reserved.

7 Record the dimensions and areas of each new shape, but do not record a shape twice. For example, a 5-inch by 2-inch rectangle should not also be recorded as a 2-inch by 5-inch rectangle.

ANSWER

Same Perimeter, Different Areas				
Name of shape	Length (l)	Width (w)	Area (A)	Perimeter (P)
Shape 1	$l = 6$ in.	$w = 1$ in.	$A = 6$ in^2	$P = 14$ in.
Shape 2	$l = 5$ in.	$w = 2$ in.	$A = 10$ in^2	$P = 14$ in.
Shape 3	$l = 4$ in.	$w = 3$ in.	$A = 12$ in^2	$P = 14$ in.

Use 1-inch square tiles or 1-inch grid paper to solve the problem.

1. Build or draw rectangles or squares that each have a perimeter of 16 inches. Use the table to record the dimensions of each shape. Then record the area of each shape.

Same Perimeter, Different Areas				
Name of shape	Length (l)	Width (w)	Area (A)	Perimeter (P)
Shape 1	$l = ?$ in.	$w = ?$ in.	$A = ?$ in^2	$P = 16$ in.
Shape 2	$l = ?$ in.	$w = ?$ in.	$A = ?$ in^2	$P = 16$ in.
Shape 3	$l = ?$ in.	$w = ?$ in.	$A = ?$ in^2	$P = 16$ in.
Shape 4	$s = ?$ in.	$s = ?$ in.	$A = ?$ in^2	$P = 16$ in.

2. Build or draw rectangles or squares that each have a perimeter of 8 inches. Use the table to record the dimensions of each shape. Then record the area of each shape.

Same Perimeter, Different Areas				
Name of shape	Length (l)	Width (w)	Area (A)	Perimeter (P)
Shape 1	$l = ?$ in.	$w = ?$ in.	$A = ?$ in.^{2}	$P = 8$ in.
Shape 2	$s = ?$ in.	$s = ?$ in.	$A = ?$ in^2	$P = 8$ in.

© K12 Inc. All rights reserved.

LEARN

Use this table to answer Problems 3 and 4.

Rectangles: Same Perimeter, Different Areas			
Name of shape	Length (*l*)	Width (*w*)	Perimeter (*P*)
Shape 1	9 in.	1 in.	20 in.
Shape 2	8 in.	2 in.	20 in.
Shape 3	7 in.	3 in.	20 in.
Shape 4	6 in.	4 in.	20 in.
Shape 5	5 in.	5 in.	20 in.

3. Which shape has an area of 24 square inches? Use an area formula to explain your answer.

4. The table shows the dimensions of four rectangles and one square that each have a perimeter of 20 inches. Could you use 1-inch square tiles to build a square with a perimeter of 18 inches? Explain your answer.

Solve.

5. A 3-centimeter by 8-centimeter mailing label has a perimeter of 22 centimeters and an area of 24 square centimeters. What are the dimensions of another label that has the same perimeter but a different area?

6. Mr. Liska decides to buy one of the banners listed below. Each has a perimeter of 18 feet. Which banner should Mr. Liska choose if he wants one with the greatest area? Explain your answer.

Color of banner	Length (*l*)	Width (*w*)	Perimeter (*P*)
Yellow	7 ft	2 ft	18 ft
Purple	5 ft	4 ft	18 ft
Orange	8 ft	1 ft	18 ft
Pink	6 ft	3 ft	18 ft

© K12 Inc. All rights reserved.

Compare Area and Perimeter

Same Area, Different Perimeters

You can use 1-inch square tiles to build rectangles or squares with the same area but different perimeters. You can also use 1-inch grid paper to draw the rectangles or squares with the same area but different perimeters. Then you can enter your data in a table to compare the perimeters of these shapes.

PROBLEM Build or draw rectangles or squares that each has an area of 16 square inches. Use the table to record the dimensions of each shape. Then record the perimeter of each shape.

Same Area, Different Perimeters				
Name of shape	Length (*l*)	Width (*w*)	Perimeter (*P*)	Area (*A*)
Shape 1	*l* = ? in.	*w* = ? in.	*P* = ? in.	*A* = 16 in²
Shape 2	*l* = ? in.	*w* = ? in.	*P* = ? in.	*A* = 16 in²
Shape 3	*s* = ? in.	*s* = ? in.	*P* = ? in.	*A* = 16 in²

SOLUTION

1 Count out 16 tiles or prepare to draw on grid paper. Build or draw a rectangle that has an area of 16 square inches.

2 Use the table to record the rectangle's dimensions. Then starting at one corner of the rectangle, count the 1-inch lengths that form a border completely around the shape, or the perimeter of the shape. You may also use a perimeter formula, such as $P = 2 \times (l + w)$. Record the perimeter of your rectangle.

3 Build or draw a second rectangle with an area of 16 square inches. Do not record a shape twice. For example, an 8-inch by 2-inch rectangle should not also be recorded as a 2-inch by 8-inch rectangle. Record the dimensions and perimeter of the second rectangle.

4 Now build or draw a square with an area of 16 square inches. Record the dimensions and perimeter of the square.

© K12 Inc. All rights reserved.

L E A R N

ANSWER

Same Area, Different Perimeters				
Name of shape	Length (*l*)	Width (*w*)	Perimeter (*P*)	Area (*A*)
Shape 1	16 in.	1 in.	34 in.	$A = 16$ in.^{2}
Shape 2	8 in.	2 in.	20 in.	$A = 16$ in^2
Shape 3	4 in.	4 in.	16 in.	$A = 16$ in^2

Use 1-inch square tiles or 1-inch grid paper to solve Problems 1 and 2.

1. Build or draw rectangles that each have an area of 20 square inches. Use the table to record the dimensions of each shape. Then record the perimeter of each shape.

Same Area, Different Perimeters				
Name of rectangle	Length (*l*)	Width (*w*)	Perimeter (*P*)	Area (*A*)
Rectangle 1	$l = ?$ in.	$w = ?$ in.	$P = ?$ in.	$A = 20$ in^2
Rectangle 2	$l = ?$ in.	$w = ?$ in.	$P = ?$ in.	$A = 20$ in^2
Rectangle 3	$l = ?$ in.	$w = ?$ in.	$P = ?$ in.	$A = 20$ in^2

2. Build or draw a rectangle and a square that each have an area of 25 square inches. Use the table to record the dimensions of each shape. Then record the perimeter of each shape.

Same Area, Different Perimeters				
Name of shape	Length (*l*)	Width (*w*)	Perimeter (*P*)	Area (*A*)
Shape 1	$l = ?$ in.	$w = ?$ in.	$P = ?$ in.	$A = 25$ in^2
Shape 2	$s = ?$ in.	$s = ?$ in.	$P = ?$ in.	$A = 25$ in^2

© K12 Inc. All rights reserved.

LEARN

Use this table to answer Problems 3 and 4.

Rectangles: Same Area, Different Perimeters			
Name of rectangle	Length (*l*)	Width (*w*)	Area (*A*)
Rectangle 1	8 in.	6 in.	48 in^2
Rectangle 2	12 in.	4 in.	48 in^2
Rectangle 3	24 in.	2 in.	48 in^2
Rectangle 4	48 in.	1 in.	48 in^2

3. Which rectangle has a perimeter of 52 inches? Use a perimeter formula to explain your answer.

4. Which rectangle has the greatest perimeter? Use a perimeter formula to explain your answer.

Solve.

5. Alexander has a garden that is 5 yards by 6 yards. He wants to make another garden with the same area but different dimensions. Should he make a garden that is 10 yards by 3 yards, or one that is 4 yards by 6 yards?

6. Rosa has two rectangular rugs in her house. The two rugs have the same area but different perimeters. Which of the following rugs could belong to Rosa? Explain your answer.

Name of rug	Length (*l*)	Width (*w*)
Blue rug	5 ft	4 ft
Red rug	9 ft	2 ft
Green rug	8 ft	2 ft
Black rug	6 ft	3 ft

© K12 Inc. All rights reserved.

LEARN

Compare Area and Perimeter

Area and Perimeter Problems

Answer the question.

1. Do these shapes have the same area or the same perimeter?

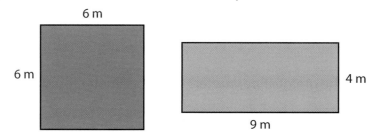

2. How are these rectangles alike and different in terms of their perimeters and areas?

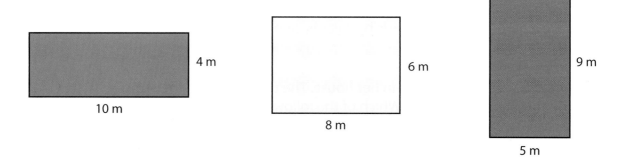

Use this rectangle to answer Problems 3 and 4.

3. Draw and label a shape that has the same perimeter but a different area.

4. Draw and label a shape that has the same area but a different perimeter.

Choose the answer.

5. Each rectangle and square with the dimensions below has a perimeter of 16 inches. Which rectangle has an area of 12 square inches?

   A. 6 in. by 2 in.

   B. 5 in. by 3 in.

   C. 4 in. by 4 in.

   D. 7 in. by 1 in.

© K12 Inc. All rights reserved.

6. Which of the following statements is true about these rectangles?

10 ft
3 ft

15 ft
2 ft

A. They have the same area but different perimeters.

B. They have the same perimeter but different areas.

C. They have different areas and perimeters.

D. They have the same areas and perimeters.

7. Which of the following statements is true about these rectangles ?

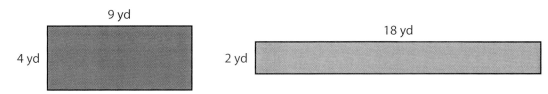

9 yd
4 yd

18 yd
2 yd

A. They have different areas and perimeters.

B. They have the same area but different perimeters.

C. They have the same areas and perimeters.

D. They have the same perimeter but different areas.

8. The listed options give the dimensions of different rectangles with an area of 60 square inches.

Which dimensions will result in the greatest perimeter?

A. 20 in. by 3 in.

B. 10 in. by 6 in.

C. 15 in. by 4 in.

D. 30 in. by 2 in.

9. A rectangle with a length of 7 feet and a width of 4 feet has an area of 28 square feet and a perimeter of 22 feet.

Which **two** rectangles have dimensions that give the same area as this rectangle but different perimeters?

A. 2 ft by 14 ft

B. 28 ft by 1 ft

C. 5 ft by 6 ft

D. 8 ft by 3 ft

10. Each option describes a rectangle with an area of 24 square centimeters.

Which dimensions describe a rectangle with a perimeter of 28 centimeters?

A. 1 cm by 24 cm

B. 2 cm by 12 cm

C. 3 cm by 8 cm

D. 4 cm by 6 cm

© K12 Inc. All rights reserved.

TRY IT

11. This square and this rectangle have equal perimeters.

Based on this information, which statement is true?

A. The figures are both squares.

B. The figures have different areas.

C. The figures have the same dimensions.

D. The figures have different angle measures.

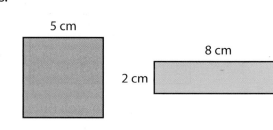

12. Which of the following statements is true about these rectangles?

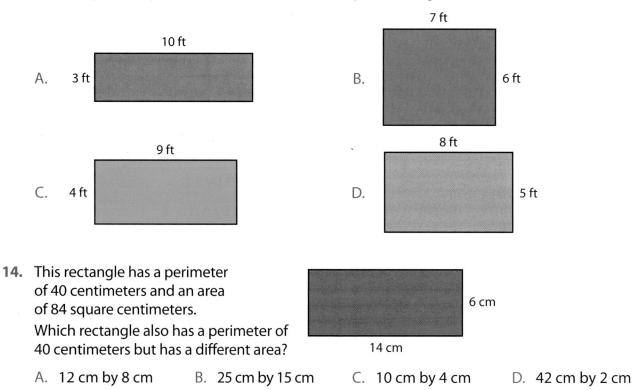

A. They have different perimeters and different areas.

B. They have different areas but the same perimeter.

C. They have the same perimeter and the same area.

D. They have the same area but different perimeters.

13. Each shape has a perimeter of 26 feet. Which shape has the greatest area?

A. 3 ft, 10 ft

B. 7 ft, 6 ft

C. 4 ft, 9 ft

D. 8 ft, 5 ft

14. This rectangle has a perimeter of 40 centimeters and an area of 84 square centimeters.

Which rectangle also has a perimeter of 40 centimeters but has a different area?

6 cm, 14 cm

A. 12 cm by 8 cm   B. 25 cm by 15 cm   C. 10 cm by 4 cm   D. 42 cm by 2 cm

© K12 Inc. All rights reserved.

TRY IT